# 11+ Verbal Reasoning

## For the **CEM** test

When it comes to the 11+, getting top marks is key — and this CGP Stretch book is packed with extra-tricky questions to help pupils aged 10-11 master the hardest parts of the test.

It starts with a section of challenging questions for each topic, so children can practise each question type. Then, there's a selection of mixed-topic Assessment Tests where they can work on really polishing their exam technique.

We've also included detailed, step-by-step answers. Everything you need!

## Stretch Practice Book
## Ages 10-11
## with Assessment Tests

# How to use this Practice Book

This book is divided into three parts — themed question practice, comprehension practice and full-length assessment tests. There are answers and detailed explanations at the back of the book.

## Themed question practice

- Each page contains practice questions divided by topic. Use these pages to work out your child's strengths and the areas they find tricky. The questions get harder down each page.
- Particularly hard questions will be marked up with a green box around the question number.
- Your child can use the smiley face tick boxes to evaluate how confident they feel with each topic.

## Comprehension practice

- This part contains questions for practising a range of comprehension skills.
  At the end of the section there are four texts with questions that test these skills.
- The texts get harder from 1-4, so don't be surprised if your child finds the later ones more tricky.

## Assessment tests

- The third part of the book contains three full-length assessment tests, each with a mix of question types from the rest of the book. They take a similar form to the real test.
- You can print multiple-choice answer sheets so your child can practise the tests as if they're sitting the real thing — visit cgpbooks.co.uk/11plus/answer-sheets or scan the QR code. →
- Use the printable answer sheets if you want your child to do each test more than once.
- If you want to give your child timed practice, give them a time limit of 30 minutes for each test, and ask them to work as quickly and carefully as they can.
- Tests 1-3 get progressively harder, so your child will probably find the later ones more challenging.
- If they haven't managed to finish the test in time, they need to work on increasing their speed, whereas if they have made a lot of mistakes, they may need to work more carefully.
- Keep track of your child's scores using the progress chart on page 78.

p.32: *The Door*, from *The Multiverse* by Andrew Wynn Owen.
    Reprinted by kind permission of Carcanet Press, Manchester, UK

p.35: Extract from *Life of Pi* by Yann Martel copyright © Yann Martel, 2001.
    Reproduced with permission of the Licensor through PLSclear.

**A note for teachers, parents and caregivers**
Just something to bear in mind if you're choosing further reading for 10-11 year olds — all the extracts in this book are suitable for children of this age, but we can't vouch for the full texts they're taken from, or other works by the same authors.

Published by CGP

Editors:
Rachel Craig-McFeely, Robbie Driscoll, Rebecca Greaves, Kirsty Sweetman, Matt Topping

With thanks to Emma Cleasby for the proofreading.
With thanks to Alice Dent for the copyright research.

Please note that CGP is not associated with CEM in any way.
This book does not include any official questions and is not endorsed by CEM.

ISBN: 978 1 78908 981 3

Printed by Elanders Ltd, Newcastle upon Tyne.
Clipart from Corel®
Based on the classic CGP style created by Richard Parsons.

Text, design, layout and original illustrations
© Coordination Group Publications Ltd. (CGP) 2022
All rights reserved.

# Contents

*Tick off the check box for each topic as you go along.*

## Section One — Making Words

Anagrams ................................................................ 2 ✓
Spelling Mistakes ................................................... 4 ☐

## Section Two — Word Meanings

Multiple Meanings .................................................. 6 ☐
Closest Meaning ..................................................... 8 ☐
Opposite Meaning ................................................ 10 ☐
Odd One Out ....................................................... 12 ☐
Reorder Words to Make a Sentence .................... 14 ☐
Word Connections ............................................... 16 ☐
Definitions ........................................................... 18 ☐

## Section Three — Completing Passages

Choose a Word ..................................................... 20 ☐
Fill in Missing Letters ............................................ 22 ☐
Choose a Sentence ............................................... 24 ☐
Choose a Phrase ................................................... 25 ☐

## Section Four — Comprehension

Finding Hidden Facts ............................................ 26 ☐
Understanding the Language in the Text ............... 28 ☐
Multiple Statement Questions — Logic .................. 30 ☐
Mixed Comprehension Questions — Text 1 ........... 32 ☐
Mixed Comprehension Questions — Text 2 ........... 35 ☐
Mixed Comprehension Questions — Text 3 ........... 38 ☐
Mixed Comprehension Questions — Text 4 ........... 41 ☐

## Assessment Tests

Test 1 .................................................................. 44 ☐
Test 2 .................................................................. 50 ☐
Test 3 .................................................................. 56 ☐

Glossary ............................................................... 62
Answers ............................................................... 63
Progress Chart ..................................................... 78

## Anagrams

Rearrange the letters in capitals to spell a word that matches the definition. Look at this example:

**CRILEGA**    A slowly moving mass of ice.   `G L A C I E R`

1. **LOBGIOY**    The scientific study of living things.

2. **URASYMM**    A short account of the main facts.

3. **EEBACRM**    To hold someone tightly.

4. **ALNIAFNIC**    Relating to money.

5. **LCOSD**    To angrily express disapproval to someone.

6. **THEBRNIAE**    To spend the winter sleeping.    / 6

7. **DELMED**    To interfere without right.

8. **ICETCCNRE**    Unusual or strange.

9. **ZAHRDAPHA**    Lacking a clear order or plan.

10. **NIIDLAYT**    In an attractive, delicate manner.

11. **LSALFESTU**    Completely free of errors.

12. **GUCINEDA**    Information given to advise.    / 6

13. **HEDTRA**    A lack of something.

14. **MLUTTU**    A loud noise made by an excited crowd.

15. **NGMTEIP**    A substance that gives paint its colour.

16. **IEADPSRAG**    To criticise in a disrespectful way.

17. **BAFCTERIA**    To manufacture something.

18. **OORGUSIR**    Extremely thorough or strict.    / 6

# Anagrams

Rearrange the letters in capitals to spell a word that completes the sentence in a sensible way. Look at this example:

Em needed **GERSYRU** after breaking her leg. ⬡S⬡U⬡R⬡G⬡E⬡R⬡Y

1. The seat next to me was **TVACNA** until Jeff sat in it. ☐☐☐☐☐☐

2. I tried to **TVDIER** the baby's attention with toys. ☐☐☐☐☐☐

3. Weather in England can be highly **BAVAILER**. ☐☐☐☐☐☐☐☐

4. Lady Olivia **VLNIYLAAT** defended her queen. ☐☐☐☐☐☐☐☐☐

5. The volcano laid **NMATDRO** for two hundred years. ☐☐☐☐☐☐☐

6. Rain seemed **NNIEMTMI** as the clouds grew darker. ☐☐☐☐☐☐☐☐  / 6

7. Woolly mammoths went **CITXTEN** more than 4000 years ago. ☐☐☐☐☐☐☐

8. The horse was **DXCAOE** out of the stable by the groom. ☐☐☐☐☐☐

9. Our manager came up with a new **YRTSATGE**. ☐☐☐☐☐☐☐☐

10. The state of Ila's room suggests she has low **NEGHEYI** standards. ☐☐☐☐☐☐☐

11. Ty can **TEIMAIT** the sound of many different bird calls. ☐☐☐☐☐☐☐

12. I gave Tom **LTCIXEPI** instructions to feed the goats. ☐☐☐☐☐☐☐☐  / 6

13. Zac was **LACDELOAT** the job of library prefect. ☐☐☐☐☐☐☐☐☐

14. My brother's **STENCASIN** whining gets on my nerves. ☐☐☐☐☐☐☐☐☐

15. Rita's food impressed even the most **SMOPUPO** of food critics. ☐☐☐☐☐☐☐

16. Li is a **YCHPEIOTR** — he claims to love nature but he litters. ☐☐☐☐☐☐☐☐☐

17. Its skin looks scaly and **IILRTEPNA**. ☐☐☐☐☐☐☐☐☐

18. Liam was praised for his **UISUJDCOI** choice. ☐☐☐☐☐☐☐☐☐  / 6

Section One — Making Words

# Spelling Mistakes

Each sentence contains a spelling mistake. Circle the letter beneath the group of words with the mistake. Look at this example:

The doctors were baffled by Ava's miraculus recovery from influenza.

| A | B | C | D |

1. Underwater missiles called torpedos can be used to devastate ships or submarines.

| A | B | C | D |

2. Caleb was convinced his ambition was acheivable, despite his friends doubting him.

| A | B | C | D |

3. To prevent a drought, we must urgently alter the public's perceptian of water usage.

| A | B | C | D |

4. Perplexed, Ama furrowed her brow as she struggled to comprehend the questionaire.

| A | B | C | D |

5. Wild swimming is invigerating but exposure to cold water can be hazardous.

| A | B | C | D |

6. Alex is a nusance — she clambers into cupboards and ambushes the pastry chef.

| A | B | C | D |

/ 6

7. Polly graciously accepted the executive's complement with a courteous smile.

| A | B | C | D |

8. Clara and Jo's easy rappor was built by endless hours of detention for disobedience.

| A | B | C | D |

9. Olga was impressed by the town's hospitality, cleanliness and efficient inferstructure.

| A | B | C | D |

10. The sailor's harrowing tale was hardly credable, yet there was no other explanation.

| A | B | C | D |

11. Though the ancient building was delapidated, its beauty was still detectable.

| A | B | C | D |

12. The deplorable criminal attempted to rest the parcel out of Laura's fierce grasp.

| A | B | C | D |

/ 6

Section One — Making Words

# Spelling Mistakes

> Each line of the following passages contains a spelling mistake.
> Circle the letter beneath the group of words with the mistake.

1. The inaugurel conference for fire dancers and associated performers took place yesterday
       A            B            C            D

2. evening.  The hotly anticipated event (conveniently located ajacent to a fire station) occurred
       A            B            C            D

3. without a hitch, with dance troops travelling far and wide to be in attendance.  It was difficult
       A            B            C            D

4. to concieve of the bewildering brilliance of talent on display — attendees included everyone
       A            B            C            D

5. from renowned alumnuses of the country's premier fire-dance institutions to earnest
       A            B            C            D

6. and conscientous beginners, eager to observe their idols and hone their craft.    ( /6 )
       A            B            C            D

7. As you reach the summit, a monumental citadel, abandoned for a millenium, rises into view.
       A            B            C            D

8. The only remaining testament to a once-great civilisation of antequity, the fortification now lies
       A            B            C            D

9. derelict, beseiged by marauding swarms of vegetation rather than human adversaries.  At its
       A            B            C            D

10. centre, a magnificent edyfice topped with spiralling turrets grabs your attention, imperiously
       A            B            C            D

11. dominating an expansive courtyard where horses once gambled and frolicked.  Though the
       A            B            C            D

12. ostentacious fortress is impoverished by neglect, a whisper of its former glory prevails in the
       A            B            C            D

13. crumbling remnants of grotesque carvings, or the pillars flecked with gold — idiosincrasies
       A            B            C            D

14. which grant a transiant yet scintillating glimpse into a bygone age of opulence.    ( /8 )
       A            B            C            D

## Multiple Meanings

Choose the word that has a similar meaning to the words in both sets of brackets. Underline your answer.

Look at this example:

(clever  intelligent)   (intense  vivid)   quick  <u>bright</u>  shiny  smart

*Hint: If you don't recognise a word, look it up in the dictionary.*

1. (merge  combine)   (trip  break)   solder  fuse  fracture  blow
2. (blanket  covering)   (hide  conceal)   canopy  shroud  shade  surround
3. (regular  uniform)   (equal  balanced)   consistent  similar  even  stable
4. (shiny  smooth)   (glamorous  stylish)   slick  superficial  fashionable  glossy
5. (line  queue)   (quarrel  altercation)   tier  row  controversy  fracas
6. (wilderness  desert)   (squander  misuse)   deplete  infertile  waste  drain

/ 6

7. (scanty  limited)   (humble  plain)   unassuming  conceited  moderate  modest
8. (bloodshed  slaughter)   (stab  impale)   puncture  butcher  gore  carnage
9. (plunge  dip)   (engage  engross)   submerge  immerse  flood  bury
10. (blend  mixture)   (aggravate  worsen)   medley  jumble  complicate  compound
11. (collection  group)   (grasp  seize)   clutch  catch  batch  bunch
12. (construct  assemble)   (vertical  straight)   pitch  upright  align  erect

/ 6

13. (deduce  surmise)   (pleasing  lovely)   figure  delight  divine  perceive
14. (link  associate)   (tell  recount)   relate  narrate  delineate  correlate
15. (wield  flaunt)   (thrive  blossom)   raise  prosper  brandish  flourish
16. (adorn  gild)   (elaborate  exaggerate)   amplify  ornament  embellish  garnish
17. (rigid  stiff)   (obstinate  stubborn)   taut  pliable  awkward  inflexible
18. (gist  sense)   (propel  shove)   direction  drift  thrust  launch

/ 6

 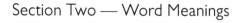

# Multiple Meanings

Choose the word that has a similar meaning to the words in both sets of brackets.  Underline your answer.

1. (capture  seizure)    (employment  job)    occupation  situation  career  possession

2. (tense  fraught)    (weary  drawn)    volatile  strained  uneasy  exhausted

3. (silhouette  profile)    (overview  summary)    shadow  review  contour  outline

4. (visit  attend)    (repeated  continual)    survey  recurrent  frequent  haunt

5. (tolerate  endure)    (appetite  inclination)    thirst  stomach  relish  swallow

6. (permission  sanction)    (depart  quit)    consent  abandon  leave  desert

7. (relationship  association)    (affix  secure)    connection  pair  join  bond

/ 7

8. (consider  ponder)    (divert  amuse)    entertain  distract  enthrall  evaluate

9. (comprehend  fathom)    (fulfil  achieve)    discern  attain  appreciate  realise

10. (distant  remote)    (eliminated  erased)    separated  banished  removed  isolated

11. (dissolve  absorb)    (grasp  understand)    consume  digest  contemplate  incorporate

12. (abdicated  quit)    (submissive  stoical)    renounced  subdued  resigned  surrendered

13. (mansion  manor)    (mass  stack)    mound  abode  pyramid  pile

14. (journalist  reporter)    (hew  cut)    hack  writer  bisect  chop

/ 7

15. (articulate  enunciate)    (declare  assert)    announce  pronounce  proclaim  decree

16. (discretion  sensitivity)    (elegance  grace)    diplomacy  finesse  delicacy  subtlety

17. (institution  establishment)    (premise  basis)    foundation  grounds  structure  rudiment

18. (superb  imposing)    (chief  foremost)    magnificent  elite  greatest  grand

19. (conducted  sent)    (defeated  conquered)    routed  vanquished  conveyed  dispelled

20. (whet  sharpen)    (refine  enhance)    grind  distil  hone  perfect

21. (attach  fasten)    (toil  labour)    implant  graft  exert  insert

/ 7

# Closest Meaning

Find the word that means the same, or nearly the same, as the word on the left.  Underline your answer.

Look at this example:

**frown**     smirk  wince  <u>scowl</u>  ridicule

1. **poisonous**     inedible  venomous  risky  acidic

2. **current**     contemporary  obsolescent  recent  original

3. **absent**     truancy  nonexistent  heedless  imaginary

4. **predict**     diagnosis  presume  appraise  foretell

5. **censor**     condemn  divulge  suspect  suppress

6. **harmony**     empathy  concord  clamour  similarity

7. **unobservant**     thoughtless  reckless  oblivious  insensitive

*Hint: Think carefully about the meaning of the word on the left before reading the options.*

/ 7

8. **passionate**     radical  devotee  smitten  fanatical

9. **contented**     gratified  ecstatic  enchanted  perturbed

10. **douse**     irrigate  ignite  drench  sprinkle

11. **nomad**     commuter  tourist  wanderer  surveyor

12. **detain**     barricade  waylay  defer  abstain

13. **renown**     celebrity  preeminent  self-esteem  mediocrity

14. **reminiscent**     expressive  memorable  enduring  evocative

/ 7

15. **sever**     cleave  allocate  divert  execute

16. **intrude**     obstruct  encroach  offend  impede

17. **condemn**     loathe  deprecate  abhor  slander

18. **suave**     debonair  civilised  influential  considerate

19. **magnificent**     conspicuous  intricate  vivacious  grandiose

20. **universal**     mandatory  unstoppable  ubiquitous  predominant

/ 6

# Closest Meaning

Complete the word on the right so that it means the same, or nearly the same, as the word on the left.

Look at this example:

**stone**   b o u l d e r

1.  **suggestion**  [ ][ ][o][p][ ][s][ ][l]
2.  **extravagant**  [w][a][ ][t][ ][ ][u][l]
3.  **respected**  [h][ ][ ][o][u][ ][e][ ]
4.  **jerk**  [ ][ ][e][n][ ][h]
5.  **urge**  [c][ ][ ][p][ ][l]
6.  **scandalous**  [ ][ ][t][ ][a][g][ ][ ][u][ ]
7.  **mechanical**  [ ][u][ ][o][m][ ][ ][i][c]

/ 7

8.  **rescue**  [s][ ][ ][v][a][ ][ ]
9.  **attractive**  [p][ ][c][ ][ ][r][e][s][ ][u][ ]
10. **copy**  [p][l][ ][g][i][ ][r][ ][s][ ]
11. **endorse**  [ ][e][c][ ][m][ ][e][ ][ ]
12. **peace**  [ ][r][a][ ][ ][u][i][ ][l][i][ ][y]
13. **worship**  [i][ ][ ][l][ ][s][ ]
14. **bored**  [j][ ][d][ ][d]

/ 7

15. **charm**  [b][ ][g][u][ ][ ][ ]
16. **underground**  [ ][u][t][ ][r][r][ ][ ][e][ ][n]
17. **apprehensive**  [t][i][ ][o][ ][o][ ][s]
18. **imperious**  [a][ ][ ][o][ ][a][ ][t]
19. **confront**  [ ][c][ ][o][ ][t]
20. **favourable**  [a][u][s][ ][ ][c][ ][ ][u][ ]

/ 6

# Opposite Meaning

Find the word that means the opposite, or nearly the opposite, of the word on the left. Underline your answer.

Look at this example:

**tighten**   consolidate  emancipate  unleash  <u>slacken</u>

1. **homemade**  formulated  amateur  manufactured  produced

2. **welcoming**  unsympathetic  sterile  congenial  inhospitable

3. **order**  government  uprising  anarchy  brawl

4. **solemn**  frivolous  dignified  artificial  blank

5. **habitual**  overdue  synchronised  distinctive  abnormal

6. **despondent**  euphoric  frantic  delirious  assured

7. **discordant**  composed  placid  harmonious  contentious

/ 7

8. **sincere**  dismissive  unreasonable  unrefined  deceitful

9. **aggravate**  mitigate  tranquillise  rehabilitate  cure

10. **sensible**  insensitive  inane  youthful  futile

11. **provoking**  uninspiring  integrating  pacifying  minimising

12. **uncritical**  discerning  perilous  wily  literate

13. **conceited**  warm  self-effacing  apologetic  embarrassed

/ 6

14. **dwindle**  invigorate  generate  proliferate  accelerate

15. **refute**  authorise  substantiate  ratify  command

16. **fresh**  hackneyed  battered  primitive  geriatric

17. **long-winded**  explicit  laconic  prudent  introverted

18. **negligent**  lax  rational  incisive  assiduous

19. **docile**  burdensome  sprightly  disobedient  vexatious

20. **anxiety**  equanimity  exasperation  despondence  jubilation

/ 7

# Opposite Meaning

Complete the word on the right so that it means the opposite, or nearly the opposite, of the word on the left.

Look at this example:

**depart**   r e m a i n

1. **apprentice**   v _ _ e _ a n
2. **biased**   i _ _ a r _ i a l
3. **keep**   f o r _ _ k _
4. **easygoing**   s _ r _ _ t
5. **enlighten**   _ o _ f o _ _ d
6. **friend**   n _ m _ _ i _
7. **smart**   s _ l o _ n _ _

Hint: Think about common word endings that might fit in the boxes to help narrow down your options — each word will have several antonyms, but only one will fit the space.

/ 7

8. **familiar**   _ l o _ f
9. **straightforward**   _ v _ s i _ e
10. **unlucky**   f o r _ _ _ o _ s
11. **praise**   d _ r _ d _
12. **worldly**   _ a _ v _
13. **innocent**   _ u l _ _ b _ e
14. **mollify**   e _ r _ g _

/ 7

15. **uncooperative**   c o m _ _ _ a n _
16. **vigour**   _ r _ i l _ y
17. **open**   f u _ _ i _ e
18. **delicious**   i _ s i _ _ d
19. **tangible**   i m _ _ i _ a r _
20. **vilify**   _ _ m m _ _ d

/ 6

# Odd One Out

Three of the words in each list are linked.  Underline the word that is not related to these three.

Look at this example:

raincoat   umbrella   <u>parasol</u>   anorak

Hint: Check your answers by working out exactly why the words are linked — for example, they might be synonyms of one another.

1.  mountain   summit   peak   apex

2.  hawk   dodo   chicken   pigeon

3.  swear   promise   pledge   claim

4.  pressurise   stimulate   motivate   inspire

5.  unearth   discover   excavate   locate

6.  professional   novice   authority   specialist

/ 6

7.  lethal   deadly   mortal   grave

8.  orator   speaker   auditor   lecturer

9.  wail   grieve   lament   mourn

10. colon   ellipsis   parentheses   article

11. suspect   convict   inmate   felon

12. forbidding   harrowing   intimidating   formidable

/ 6

13. fortress   moat   drawbridge   portcullis

14. offspring   organism   brood   young

15. tyrant   monarch   despot   dictator

16. mystery   romance   dystopian   biography

17. halt   freeze   standstill   cease

18. saying   cliché   maxim   proverb

/ 6

Section Two — Word Meanings

# Odd One Out

> Three of the words in each list are linked.
> Underline the word that is not related to these three.

1. eager   always   immediately   rarely

2. jubilation   vexation   elation   exhilaration

3. vacillate   hesitate   dither   negotiate

4. crocus   hyacinth   daffodil   willow

5. vanity   hubris   allure   pride

6. visual   observable   visible   apparent

7. forthright   candid   impromptu   frank

/ 7

8. bait   hook   stalk   rod

9. cremate   incinerate   burn   ignite

10. Argentina   Mongolia   Brazil   Chile

11. wind   nuclear   power   solar

12. flute   oboe   trombone   clarinet

13. copious   abundant   profuse   sumptuous

14. mingle   socialise   combine   coalesce

/ 7

15. inessential   inherent   intrinsic   fundamental

16. sagacious   canny   astute   discreet

17. thwart   delay   foil   prevent

18. forefront   semblance   facade   veneer

19. femur   ligament   humerus   patella

20. Birmingham   York   Cardiff   Dublin

21. chronology   epoch   era   period

22. fussy   gaudy   dilated   overwrought

/ 8

Section Two — Word Meanings

# Reorder Words to Make a Sentence

> Rearrange the words so that each sentence makes sense.
> Underline the word which doesn't fit into the sentence.
>
> Look at this example:
>
> playing <u>very</u> Katya hockey likes
>
> The remaining words can be arranged into the sentence:
> **Katya likes playing hockey.**

1. someone know wears pink shirt who only I clothes

2. be a to but I want I sailor get aboard seasick

3. the missed was concert delayed the by so we bus

4. not since dentist was the he before has Charlie eight seen

5. the repair a because road blocked traffic is accident there was

6. three started in Priya old competing years ago gymnastics

/ 6

7. reading book the cliffhanger I on thrilling a chapters ended was

8. I my thinks sister person most am dullest ever the that

9. munched the to juicy naughty eat refused carrot horse the

10. got chose dressed her Tina outfit and once then

11. paused she Jodie the loudly not the like did because song lyrics

12. and its rose entire applauded to cheer audience feet the

/ 6

13. join club for is new the members local advertising rowing

14. went begins for we before a it rain walk started to

15. in Leo were feet blisters sting covered his ran until

16. party a cake my was burning success the despite failure

17. more sport an seems it exciting be fishing boring but can

18. jungle explorer trekked adventurous cliff the the dangerous through

/ 6

# Reorder Words to Make a Sentence

Rearrange the words so that each sentence makes sense.
Underline the word which doesn't fit into the sentence.

1. has am because on excited cactus a my flower leaves I bloomed

2. Kamil strict teacher for on daydreaming lesson told during the off her

3. down but earlier arrived broke train liked their have they would

4. since favourite we every our sampled chose type cake we before of

5. care the during in school when take from dark back walking

6. too the so burger it was told let I brother filling finish my

7. noises went computer ends screen my then and started black the making

 / 7

8. rolling in in puddle after us mud at a dog our covered

9. I who at complimented kind my smiled the T-shirt its green girl

10. make in a sauce to you dipping melt must chocolate pour order

11. English Viv that in should lesson realised was be meant to she an

12. damage failed illegible its address the arrive because letter to was

13. hundred cycle managed pounds sponsored raise two to Katy cousin's my

14. hotly a not anticipated bit disappointment the was of contest a

 / 7

15. wildly my due the maths gesticulating explain I homework by attempted of to absence

16. complete Sam managed without to the Sally's puzzle would those not expertise have

17. closer the tiger from was it enclosure as clear was we moved enraged away the

18. scolded meant was be when I sitting to jokes was silence telling for in by I

19. van flooded children ice heard into street the excited the the when shouted cream they

20. long there school break in is favourite from my season because is summer a

21. prefer stroked dogs walks or how long you that being on do going think

 / 8

22. young their they and parents them like cool they once believe were cannot that

Section Two — Word Meanings

# Word Connections

Underline the word in the set of brackets that completes the sentence in the most sensible way.

Look at this example:

**Leopard** is to **spot** as **zebra** is to (<u>stripe</u>  leap  see  pattern).

1. **Cascade** is to **flow** as (completion  finish  ending  commence) is to **cease**.

2. **Fish** are to **school** as **bats** are to (pack  band  herd  colony).

3. (Illicit  Legitimate  Dishonest  Prohibit) is to **legal** as **precarious** is to **secure**.

4. **Cheerful** is to **disconsolate** as **sociable** is to (hermit  reclusive  amicable  wary).

5. **Doctor** is to **medicine** as **editor** is to (finance  publishing  fiction  magazine).

6. (Ravine  Cavity  Cavern  River) is to **gorge** as **precipice** is to **cliff**.

7. **Knight** is to **quest** as **agent** is to (intelligence  mission  spy  disguise).

/ 7

8. **Spectator** is to (stadium  match  watch  cheer) as **audience** is to **play**.

9. **Traffic** is to **pollution** as **logging** is to (deforestation  sewage  litter  diversity).

10. **Bolt** is to **wrench** as (mallet  nail  knock  screw) is to **hammer**.

11. (Sonar  Darkness  Night  Lunar) is to **moon** as **solar** is to **sun**.

12. **Impulsive** is to **rash** as (pragmatic  responsible  direct  diligent) is to **practical**.

13. (Dialogue  Speech  Journal  Performance) is to **persuade** as **report** is to **inform**.

/ 7

14. **Gale** is to (wind  breeze  tornado  blow) as **downpour** is to **drizzle**.

15. **Threatening** is to **innocuous** as **hostile** is to (averse  gentle  benign  balmy).

16. **Deceit** is to **fraud** as (status  lowliness  reverence  disappointment) is to **prestige**.

17. **Slothful** is to (impassive  proactive  determined  energetic) as **significant** is to **trifling**.

18. (Chair  Throne  Pew  Seat) is to **chapel** as **sofa** is to **lounge**.

19. **Prose** is to (novel  sonnet  lyric  fiction) as **verse** is to **poem**.

20. **Withdraw** is to **revoke** as **defend** is to (attack  uphold  struggle  dispel).

/ 6

Section Two — Word Meanings

# Word Connections

> Underline the word in the set of brackets that completes the sentence in the most sensible way.

1. **Barrier** is to **prevent** as **aqueduct** is to (bridge   enable   stream   convey).

2. **Creative** is to (ingenious   insightful   artist   unorthodox) as **wise** is to **informed**.

3. **Exercise** is to **muscular** as **study** is to (knowledgeable   revision   mentality   ignorant).

4. (Spite   Goodwill   Charity   Respect) is to **malice** as **generosity** is to **avarice**.

5. **Plethora** is to (sufficiency   plentiful   lack   excess) as **variety** is to **diversity**.

6. **Mermaid** is to **fish** as (fawn   centaur   unicorn   sphinx) is to **horse**.

7. **Strut** is to **cockerel** as (flit   soar   plummet   flutter) is to **eagle**.

/ 7

8. **Nuptials** are to **couple** as **graduation** is to (academic   student   university   crowd).

9. **Calculator** is to **compute** as **compass** is to (point   spin   explore   navigate).

10. **Exalted** is to (exciting   reputed   sublime   profound) as **dire** is to **abysmal**.

11. (Enlighten   Mystify   Rectify   Amend) is to **perplex** as **dishearten** is to **uplift**.

12. **Achievement** is to **celebrate** as **failure** is to (tolerate   console   confess   displease).

13. **Shrug** is to (careless   nonchalant   jubilant   enraged) as **tremble** is to **afraid**.

/ 7

14. **Unanimous** is to **united** as **frail** is to (robust   frugal   infirm   elderly).

15. **Skip** is to (trudge   roam   dance   stumble) as **enthuse** is to **mutter**.

16. **Poignant** is to **affecting** as **affected** is to (convinced   pretentious   dissembling   different).

17. (Soldier   Campaigner   Pacifist   General) is to **war** as **vegetarian** is to **meat**.

18. **Bovine** is to **cows** as **porcine** is to (goats   sheep   porcupines   pigs).

19. **Terrestrial** is to **Earth** as **celestial** is to (hell   ocean   space   atmosphere).

20. **Decency** is to **decorum** as (guile   adversity   candour   enigmatic) is to **cunning**.

21. **Heart** is to **circulatory** as **brain** is to (nervous   respiratory   mind   head).

/ 8

22. **Apoplectic** is to (rueful   placid   raving   contrite) as **goad** is to **calm**.

Section Two — Word Meanings

# Definitions

> Look at the definition on the left. Underline the word on the right that best matches the definition.
>
> Look at this example:
>
> **to long for**  love <u>yearn</u> urge incline

1. **width or span**  height breadth scale radius
2. **floor of a fireplace**  embers foot hearth furnace
3. **to become shrivelled**  dwindle burgeon evaporate wither
4. **a complete failure**  disappointment peril fiasco adversity
5. **extremely beautiful**  pretty charismatic comely idyllic
6. **rough and harsh**  corrosive terse abrasive destructive
7. **a heavy fall of rain**  deluge hurricane spray tsunami

/ 7

8. **wild or untamed**  cultivated inhospitable brutal feral
9. **to officially seize**  blockade confiscate purloin sanction
10. **a heated disagreement**  feud bickering altercation friction
11. **the state of being violent**  ferocity predatory atrocity benignity
12. **gradual destruction by weather**  decay erosion disintegration climate
13. **to organise an exhibition**  curate unveil devise appraise
14. **bizarre or unusual**  inventive outlandish fanciful notable

 / 7

15. **filled with intense passion**  motivated preoccupied infatuated engrossed
16. **extremely small**  minor petite insignificant diminutive
17. **wanting to do harm**  diabolical deprecating malignant unsympathetic
18. **feeling great loss**  bereft impotent impoverished denigrated
19. **shining and glossy**  garish lustrous iridescent bright
20. **situated on the edge**  confines outside median peripheral

 / 6

# Definitions

> Look at the definition on the left. Underline the word on the right that best matches the definition.

1. **a follower or supporter**  obsessive cohort guru adherent

2. **a jarring mix of sounds**  discordant symphony cacophony turbulence

3. **a small model of a human**  sculpture replica stereotype figurine

4. **to swing back and forth**  lurch fluctuate oscillate dislocate

5. **relentlessly gloomy**  unbending crestfallen dour discouraged

6. **to destroy utterly**  annihilate blight sabotage dismantle

7. **a lack of ability**  incapacitated ineptitude incapable deficiency

/ 7

8. **to spare from punishment**  reprieve yield abate subside

9. **an unwelcome consequence**  aftermath repercussion product reverberation

10. **modest and shy**  apologetic tolerable submissive demure

11. **a final demand**  ultimatum pact term requirement

12. **extremely difficult and tiring**  debilitating obscure onerous perplexing

13. **rasping and throaty**  stifled brusque piercing guttural

14. **to come from**  emigrate instigate emanate inaugurate

/ 7

15. **having doubts or reservations**  rational sceptical pessimistic cynical

16. **wanting to seek revenge**  petrifying intimidatory vindictive antagonising

17. **respected due to age or wisdom**  idolised venerable cherished ancient

18. **a subtle difference**  inconsistency nuance imbalance variation

19. **having mature qualities at a young age**  precocious genius sagacious juvenile

20. **aggressive and willing to fight**  unruly zealous audacious belligerent

21. **shy and lacking self-confidence**  diffident demeaned coy conscious

22. **a saying or proverb**  adage hypothesis slogan remark

/ 8

## Choose a Word

Choose the correct words to complete each passage below.

1. ☐ have
   ☐ could
   ☐ will
   ☐ had
   never understood the

I

2. ☐ mystery
   ☐ appeal
   ☐ aptitude
   ☐ display
   of ballet until I watched a performance

of *Swan Lake* recently. Expecting to be bored by the

3. ☐ absence
   ☐ duration
   ☐ monotony
   ☐ wealth
   of dialogue, I was

4. ☐ apathetic
   ☐ captivating
   ☐ spellbound
   ☐ perplexed
   from the moment the silent dancers

5. ☐ appeared
   ☐ sprang
   ☐ twirl
   ☐ started
   into life.

/ 5

A poet laureate is a poet who is

6. ☐ distinctively
   ☐ precisely
   ☐ hopefully
   ☐ specially
   appointed by a government or other official

7. ☐ leader
   ☐ expert
   ☐ country
   ☐ body
   . In the UK,

8. ☐ however
   ☐ despite
   ☐ after
   ☐ although
   the position

9. ☐ entails
   ☐ envelops
   ☐ engages
   ☐ endorses
   no official duties, the

poet laureate is

10. ☐ mandated
    ☐ loathe
    ☐ expected
    ☐ compelled
    to compose poems to mark national events.

/ 5

My

11. ☐ previous
    ☐ stringent
    ☐ newfound
    ☐ long-standing
    interest in volcanoes can be

12. ☐ tailed
    ☐ trailed
    ☐ traced
    ☐ taken
    back to my childhood.

When I was ten, my mother, a

13. ☐ scientist
    ☐ study
    ☐ geology
    ☐ lifelong
    graduate with a

14. ☐ knowledge
    ☐ passion
    ☐ enthusiasm
    ☐ devotion
    for volcanology,

took me to Iceland, one of the most volcanically

15. ☐ bustling
    ☐ active
    ☐ charging
    ☐ activated
    places in the world.

/ 5

# Choose a Word

Choose the correct words to complete each passage below.

Located in Poole Harbour on the south coast of England, Brownsea Island is

1. ☐ open
   ☐ exclusive   to
   ☐ home
   ☐ known

an

2. ☐ abundance
   ☐ increase
   ☐ outpouring
   ☐ extent

of wildlife, including several protected

3. ☐ areas
   ☐ species   of bird, as well
   ☐ colonies
   ☐ classes

as the rare red squirrel.

4. ☐ Nevertheless
   ☐ Specifically   , the island is notable for playing
   ☐ Additionally
   ☐ Fortunately

5. ☐ party
   ☐ host   to
   ☐ up
   ☐ along

the first Scout Camp in 1907, and the island is usually regarded as the

6. ☐ essence
   ☐ product   of the
   ☐ antithesis
   ☐ birthplace

modern-day Scouting and Guiding movements.

/ 6

---

Bella stared down at the chessboard, a look of intense concentration

**7.** ☐ wrinkled
   ☐ embossed   on her
   ☐ etched
   ☐ adorned

face. The game, which was

**8.** ☐ receding
   ☐ teetering   towards its conclusion, was finely
   ☐ lingering
   ☐ inching

**9.** ☐ poised
   ☐ fought   :
   ☐ contested
   ☐ honed

Bella had

**10.** ☐ equal
   ☐ fewer   pieces remaining but was in a stronger
   ☐ more
   ☐ less

**11.** ☐ imperative
   ☐ critical   position.
   ☐ strategic
   ☐ physical

Despite her efforts to focus on the board, she was

**12.** ☐ obscurely
   ☐ excitedly   aware of the ticking of the
   ☐ serenely
   ☐ acutely

/ 6

clock beside her. At last, taking a deep breath, she made her move.

Section Three — Completing Passages

# Fill in Missing Letters

Fill in the missing letters to complete the words in the following passages.

1. Humans first travelled to the South Pole in 1911, when an e☐☐edi☐☐on led by

2. veteran Norwegian explorer Roald Amundsen su☐☐☐☐ded in reaching Earth's

3. southernmost point. Amundsen, along with four co☐☐a☐☐ons , several sledges

4. and over fifty dogs, set off from his base on the edge of the Antarctic ☐ont☐n☐nt in

5. October, arrived at the pole in mid-December and returned ☐af☐☐y in late January.

6. That same winter, a ☐iva☐ team led by British naval officer Robert Scott also

7. reached the pole, but sadly none of the party s☐☐☐ived the return journey.

/ 7

8. Zain lifted his head and sc☐☐tin☐sed the moody sky with a look of concern.

9. He watched a fat raindrop plu☐☐☐t to earth, landing with a soft plink on the tin

10. roof of a ☐ea☐b☐ cowshed. It was quickly followed by another, and then another,

11. until Zain found himself facing a ba☐☐age of bullet-like raindrops, each one faster

12. and fatter than the last. Desperately pulling his already so☐d☐n hood over his head,

13. he rushed across the field in the ☐ire☐☐ion of home, trying his utmost not

14. to lose his footing on the in☐☐e☐☐ingly muddy ground.

/ 7

15. If you ask people to name famous London ☐an☐☐arks , few will fail to mention

16. Big Ben, one of the most i☐oni☐ sights in the city. Strictly speaking, the name

17. 'Big Ben' refers only to the enormous bell wi☐☐☐n the clock tower, but it is

18. commonly used to refer to the tower as a whole. The clock, which is f☐m☐d for its

19. accuracy, was in☐☐a☐☐ed together with the bell in 1859 and has marked time

20. for the people of London ever since. The clock must be w☐☐nd three times a

21. week, a ☐ro☐e☐s which takes more than an hour.

/ 7

Section Three — Completing Passages

# Fill in Missing Letters

Fill in the missing letters to complete the words in the following passages.

1. Shuffling reluctantly into the front room at her mother's re◻u◻◻t , Ava tried to force

2. her lips into a smile.  S◻◻t◻d between her parents on the sofa was a tall, thin lady

3. dressed in a dull white blouse and an ◻qu◻◻ly dull grey skirt that reached almost

4. to the floor.  She had a long, bony nose and a◻g◻l◻r cheekbones so pronounced

5. that it looked as if they were ca◻◻ed from stone.  Her hair, which was as grey

6. as her skirt, hung down limply, f◻◻min◻ her face like a pair of curtains.

7. Most un◻◻◻ving of all were her beady black eyes, which she fixed on Ava.

/ 7

8. The terms 'canoe' and 'kayak' are often used in◻◻◻cha◻◻◻ably , but they are

9. not the same thing.  Typically, a canoe is an open v◻◻s◻l , whereas kayaks are

10. e◻◻lose◻ with a hole in the middle for the paddler to climb in and out of.

11. Another cr◻◻◻al difference is the style of paddle: a canoeist uses a single-bladed

12. paddle, whereas a kayak is pr◻◻◻◻led forward by a double-bladed paddle.

13. The two craft do have ◻im◻l◻◻◻ties , however.  For example, both can

14. be made of various materials, such as wood, plastic and al◻◻◻n◻um .

/ 7

15. I was woken by a delicate ◻ha◻t of sunlight glinting through the tiny cabin window.

16. Half-opening one eye, I lay i◻◻o◻ile , listening to the gentle murmur of the ocean

17. and the ◻◻◻thm◻c chug of the engine as the ship glided onwards.  After a while,

18. I stirred and, managing at last to ext◻◻◻c◻◻e myself from the warm embrace of the

19. duvet, got to my feet.  As I padded over to the window, it o◻◻◻◻re◻ to me that

20. we must now be far out at sea, and I ◻ui◻◻◻n◻d my step, eager to set

21. eyes on the ◻◻pan◻◻ of azure ocean that waited beyond the glass.

/ 7

Section Three — Completing Passages

# Choose a Sentence

Choose the sentence that best fits the gap in each passage.
Circle the letter of the correct answer.

1.  The air in the courtyard was heavy with the stench of sewage, which had spilled out of the drains in several places and lay in thick pools, festering in the midday sun.  Jared emerged from a doorway. _____ It seemed he was oblivious to the awful sight and pungent smell.

    A  He produced a bottle of perfume and sprayed it liberally around him, to little effect.
    B  Carefully, he picked his way around the puddles of filth, tutting to himself as he went.
    C  Whistling merrily, he strolled leisurely across the cobblestones, lost in his own thoughts.
    D  Wrinkling his nose, he grimaced and immediately retreated into the building.

2.  As she raced across the bustling station lobby, Imani heard the loudspeaker chime:
    "Last call for the 11:55 train to Wigan, departing from Platform 4." _____
    "I'm so sorry!" she gasped, casting the man a remorseful look but hardly slowing her pace.

    A  Finding her path blocked, she shoved a man out of the way defiantly.
    B  She was in such a hurry that she didn't notice knocking a man's sandwich out of his hand.
    C  Breaking into a run, she collided with a man, sending him sprawling.
    D  Realising she wasn't going to make it, she stopped rushing and turned to her companion.

3.  There is a wide range of eating establishments in our town, from pizzerias and pubs to Chinese restaurants and chip shops. _____ There used to be one on the high street, but it recently closed down and new owners have not yet been found.

    A  The only thing missing is a Mexican restaurant.
    B  We've just got our first restaurant serving Georgian cuisine.
    C  However, we've never had a Thai restaurant.
    D  Despite all this, there isn't a single place that serves pizza.

4.  After much anticipation, *The Penguins of Pimlico*, a brand-new musical, debuted on the West End last night.  Reviews were mixed. _____ However, many felt that this was offset by the quality of the music and the incredible talent of the cast.

    A  Most reviewers considered the plot to be so incomprehensible that it ruined the show.
    B  Most reviewers thought the story was too convoluted.
    C  Most reviewers praised the set design and costumes.
    D  Most reviewers were critical of the standard of singing.

/ 4

# Choose a Phrase

Choose the phrase that best fits each gap in the passages below.

Andy paced nervously to and fro.

1. ☐ He paused briefly to listen
☐ The draught made him shiver , causing beads of sweat
☐ The air in the room was stifling
☐ He took a few deep breaths

to gather on his wrinkled brow. He stared

2. ☐ intently at the door
☐ blankly at the ceiling , evidently expecting it
☐ anxiously at the clock
☐ calmly at the window

to open at any moment. Finally, he heard footsteps

3. ☐ tiptoeing up to the door
☐ thundering along the corridor , and
☐ slowly passing by
☐ cautiously approaching

the headteacher marched purposefully into the room with

4. ☐ a panicked look
☐ a sympathetic smile on her face.
☐ an enormous grin
☐ a grave expression

/ 4

"Andy, I'm afraid this is the last straw," she snapped. "You're being excluded."

---

After heavy rainfall, the town of Kildy is at risk of severe flooding this week, leading many residents

to

5. ☐ abandon their flooded homes
☐ seek compensation for damages . Although the water has not yet breached the flood
☐ bemoan the lack of flood defences
☐ temporarily leave their homes

prevention mechanisms, evacuations were carried out

6. ☐ as a precaution
☐ agonisingly slowly , since the water
☐ as a last resort
☐ in just a few places

levels are expected to continue rising

7. ☐ for the next fortnight
☐ in the coming days . Meteorologists have predicted
☐ throughout the winter
☐ almost indefinitely

drier weather by next week, but in the meantime,

8. ☐ it's thought the rain will abate
☐ residents are returning home .
☐ forecasts remain uncertain / 4
☐ the outlook is gloomy

Section Three — Completing Passages

# Finding Hidden Facts

Read the information carefully, then use it to answer the question that follows. Write your answer on the line.

Hint: It can help to draw a table with all the information in.
Watch out for repeated information — don't count anything twice.

1.  Lacey, Amber, Isaac, Tyler and Honoka are eating an Indian takeaway.

    Everyone except Lacey has a curry. While the others are eating their curry, Lacey has some aloo gobi and a samosa. Tyler, Amber and Isaac all eat some naan bread. Isaac is the only one who eats a poppadom. Honoka has some aloo gobi and a curry. Amber, Tyler and Lacey are the only children who try some of the chutney.

    Who eats the **fewest** types of food? _____

2.  Scott, Imogen, Abdul, Grace and Stanley are discussing the local castles they have visited.

    Everyone except Imogen has been to Alnwick Castle. Imogen visited both Edlingham Castle and Chillingham Castle with Abdul. Stanley, Grace and Scott have all been to Bamburgh Castle, but Grace and Abdul are the only children to have visited Lindisfarne Castle. Scott and Stanley both visited Edlingham Castle on the same day they went to Alnwick Castle.

    Who has visited the **most** castles? _____

3.  Joey, Aarya, Leo, Eva and Zachary have spent a weekend together mountain biking.

    Four of the children rode on the purple trail. Everyone except Zachary rode on the yellow trail. Zachary rode on the blue trail straight after finishing the red trail, while Aarya was the only one who rode on the white trail. Leo was the only child not to ride on the blue trail. Joey wanted to ride on the purple trail but ran out of time.

    Who rode on the **most** trails? _____

4.  Isla, Todd, Lily, Adamu and Carys are collecting dinosaur figurines.

    Only Adamu has the pterodactyl, but he doesn't yet have the velociraptor. Lily, Adamu and Isla all have the tyrannosaurus. Todd has the triceratops. Three of the children have the velociraptor. Everyone except Todd has the stegosaurus. The only figurines Carys has are the tyrannosaurus, the stegosaurus and the triceratops.

    Who has the **fewest** dinosaur figurines? _____

/ 4

# Finding Hidden Facts

Read the information carefully, then use it to answer the question that follows. Write your answer on the line.

1. Brooke, Jakub, Xiu, Lucia and Peter are discussing the flowers they've grown in their gardens.

   Three people have pansies in their garden. Jakub is the only one who doesn't have roses. Brooke has carnations and tulips, but she doesn't have any pansies. The only flowers in Peter's garden are tulips, carnations and roses. Everyone except Lucia and Peter has daffodils. Xiu and Lucia both have tulips and orchids in their gardens.

   Who has the **most** types of flowers?  _____

2. Niall, Muhammad, Roisin, Aayat and Antoine are at a water park.

   The only one of the park's five slides Roisin doesn't go on is Splash City. Aayat and Muhammad go on Splash City and River Race. Antoine goes on more than half of the slides. Everyone except Muhammad goes on Neptune's Revenge. Only two children go on the Twizzler. Roisin and Niall are the only ones to go on Torpedo Run. Everyone except Antoine goes on River Race.

   Who goes on the **fewest** slides?  _____

3. Yusuf, Oli, Sienna, Fatima and Lola went to a film festival.

   There were five short films, all shown in different screens. Sienna and Fatima enjoyed 'Curse of the Koala', but none of the children watched 'Rainbow Child'. Oli watched 'The Final Passengers' in Screen 2, then joined Fatima to watch 'The Galaxy's Core' in Screen 4, whilst Yusuf and Lola chose to watch 'World Cup Wonder' in Screen 3 instead. Everyone except Yusuf watched the film in Screen 5.

   Who watched the **most** films?  _____

4. Scarlett, Rhys, Shivansh, Arthur and Emily are talking about the clubs they do after school.

   There is one club on each day from Monday to Friday. Scarlett and Rhys are the only ones who go to Friday science club and the only ones who don't play hockey. Three of the children play badminton on Tuesday, and everyone except Rhys plays volleyball on Thursday. Two of the children go to art club. Scarlett only goes to clubs on Tuesday, Thursday and Friday. Shivansh goes to three clubs, including badminton. Emily only goes to the sports clubs.

   Who goes to the **fewest** clubs?  _____

   / 4

# Understanding the Language in the Text

Read the passage below, then answer the questions that follow.
Underline the correct option for each question.

In the early months of Ada's imprisonment, she had spent entire days pacing furiously up and down her cell, pausing only to beat her palms in frustration against the grimy walls, which seemed to be forever closing in around her. Now, she would sit motionless, her mind grasping faintly at increasingly distant memories that served as her only weapon against the

5 creeping tide of emptiness that threatened to overwhelm her.

She had grown so accustomed to darkness that the light which she once craved was now hateful to her. Once a day, the heavy iron door of her cell would scrape open, flooding the interior with a blinding light that sent her scurrying into the darkest corner like a woodlouse cruelly exposed by the lifting of a log. She would crouch in a daze, while

10 the jailer, who tried never to meet her eye, hastily thrust her measly rations into her hands. Moments later, the door slammed shut. The tedium of this dismal routine numbed Ada's mind to such an extent that it was some time before she began to notice the subtle changes in the jailer's behaviour.

1. The author says that the walls "seemed to be forever closing in around" Ada (line 3). This suggests that her cell is:

   A dingy and sordid.  B cramped and oppressive.  C intricate and disorienting.

2. At the end of the passage, Ada starts noticing "subtle changes in the jailer's behaviour" (lines 12-13). What effect does this have on the reader?

   A It builds anticipation.  B It creates sympathy for Ada.  C It highlights Ada's isolation.

3. Ada's memories are "her only weapon against the creeping tide of emptiness" (lines 4-5). This suggests that she needs her memories to:

   A remind her how to fight.  B stop her from falling asleep.  C keep her mind engaged.

4. The jailer tries not to "meet" Ada's eye (line 10). What does this suggest about him?

   A He feels guilty.  B He is afraid of Ada.  C He wants to help Ada.

5. The author compares Ada to a "woodlouse" (line 9). This emphasises how:

   A she has spent so long in the prison that she no longer wants to escape.
   B she can hardly remember anything about her life before she was imprisoned.
   C she is being treated as though she isn't human.

/ 5

# Understanding the Language in the Text

> Read the passage below, then answer the questions that follow.
> Underline the correct option for each question.

"Pull up! Pull up! We're dropping too fast!" Lucien bellowed. He clenched the overhead handle with one enormous, white-knuckled hand and rested the other on the holster holding his laser gun, as if drawing the weapon might somehow help to stabilise the spiralling spaceship.

5   "I know what I'm doing," came Astra's clipped response. Despite the alarming angle of the ship's trajectory and the startling judders of the choking engines, she manipulated the controls as assuredly as ever. With her eyes fixed forward, she sent the ship pitching to the left, apparently finding some obscure waymarker in the impenetrable cloud of crimson dust.

Lucien was just about to reach for the main controls when, as if someone had turned
10  the page of an enormous pop-up book, the swirling ocean of dust vanished, and the wrinkled surface of a vast desert planet took its place. At once, Astra sent the ship into a stomach-churning upward curve. Only when it was level did she at last turn to Lucien.

"I'm glad you have so much faith in me," she grinned.

1.  When she is driving, Astra has "her eyes fixed forward" (line 7). This suggests that she:
    **A** feels very nervous.      **B** is highly focused.      **C** is afraid of Lucien.

2.  When the surface of the planet appears, it is "as if someone had turned the page of an enormous pop-up book" (lines 9-10). What impression does this create of the planet?
    **A** It appears very suddenly.      **B** It can be seen in detail.      **C** It doesn't seem real.

3.  Lucien holds onto the handle with a "white-knuckled hand" (line 2). This suggests that he:
    **A** is angry with Astra.      **B** is extremely strong.      **C** feels frightened.

4.  Why does Astra say, "I'm glad you have so much faith in me" (line 13)?
    **A** She is grateful to Lucien.      **B** She's being ironic.      **C** She is exaggerating.

5.  The author describes "the startling judders of the choking engines" (line 6).
    What does this suggest about them?
    **A** They are struggling to function in the cloud of dust.
    **B** They have fallen silent and are in danger of stopping.
    **C** They are making a loud, rhythmic noise but still working.

/ 5

# Multiple Statement Questions — Logic

> Read the information carefully, then use it to answer the question that follows. Underline the correct answer.

> Hint: Write down the people's names at the start. Then, as you read, make a note of all the information you learn about each person next to their name.

1. Jayden, Maisie, Qadir, Charlotte and George played crazy golf. The lowest score won. Charlotte's score was higher than Jayden's. George didn't have the highest score. Maisie and Qadir got the same score. Only one person got a lower score than Jayden.

   Which one of the sentences below **cannot** be true?

   **A** Charlotte finished in last place.
   **B** Jayden's score was lower than Maisie's.
   **C** Qadir and Maisie were joint winners.
   **D** Qadir's score was higher than Charlotte's.

2. Lexi, Finn, Zayd, Imogen and Bella take it in turns to cook each night from Monday to Sunday. Everyone cooks at least once. Finn cooks on Monday, and then again on Sunday. Lexi cooks on Wednesday. Bella cooks two days in a row. Zayd cooks later in the week than Lexi.

   Which one of the sentences below **must** be true?

   **A** Imogen cooks on Tuesday.
   **B** Lexi cooks on Friday.
   **C** Zayd cooks on Saturday.
   **D** Bella cooks on Tuesday.

3. Precious, Riley, Erin, Bobby and Cheng have been selling raffle tickets for charity. Erin raised £18. Precious raised £5, which was less than anyone else. Riley raised £15. Bobby raised less than Riley but twice as much as Cheng. Riley raised the second highest amount of money.

   Which one of the sentences below **cannot** be true?

   **A** Cheng raised £6.
   **B** Erin raised the most money.
   **C** Riley raised more than Precious and Cheng combined.
   **D** Bobby raised £9.

/ 3

# Multiple Statement Questions — Logic

Read the information carefully, then use it to answer the question that follows. Underline the correct answer.

1. Chloe, Maryam, Jude, Amelia and Jack all moved house in different months of the year 2020. Jude moved house in August, two months after Jack and at least 6 months after Amelia. Maryam moved later in the year than Jack, but she wasn't the last person to move. Chloe moved three months after Amelia.

Which one of the sentences below **cannot** be true?

A Chloe moved house in April.

B No one moved house after August.

C Maryam moved house four months after Amelia.

D Amelia moved house five months before Jack.

2. Luca, Niamh, Kasun, Phoebe and Tomos are comparing how long their journeys to school take. Kasun's journey takes the longest. Niamh's journey takes five minutes longer than Luca's. Tomos's journey takes 20 minutes. Phoebe's journey takes twice as long as Luca's but less time than Tomos's.

Which one of the sentences below **must** be true?

A Kasun's journey takes more than 30 minutes.

B Phoebe's journey takes more than 15 minutes.

C Niamh's journey takes less than 15 minutes.

D Luca's journey takes less than 5 minutes.

3. Paige, Zeynep, Harry, Elias and Freya took part in an orienteering challenge. They got 10 points for visiting checkpoints with a blue flag and 20 points for visiting checkpoints with a red flag. Elias won with a score of 180 points. Freya visited 10 blue checkpoints, which was more than anyone else, but she scored fewer points than Paige. Everyone visited at least 2 red checkpoints, and Elias visited 5, which was the most. Zeynep and Harry both scored 80 points.

Which one of the sentences below **must** be true?

A Paige visited more blue checkpoints than Zeynep.

B Freya scored fewer than 140 points.

C Elias and Paige visited the same number of red checkpoints.

D Harry and Zeynep visited the same number of blue checkpoints.

 / 3

# Mixed Comprehension Questions — Text 1

Read the poem below, then answer the questions that follow.

## The Door

Distracting rays were shining round my door
    And so I stood
  And stepped across the landing floor
  To see if any light-source could
5    Be ascertained but, once I was outside,
    I checked my stride.

Out there I found a stretching corridor,
    So down I walked.
  I had not noticed it before.
10    On every lintel, names were chalked
And soon I stalled at one that was well-known:
    It was my own.

The hinges creaked. I cautiously went in,
    Enjoying there
15    A room where sunlight lapped my skin
  And central was a swivel chair.
It spun about. I felt a smile extend:
    'Good morning, friend.'

This figure gestured me towards an arch
20    Marked 'Happiness'
  And I, determined, moved to march
  Its way, but paused: 'I should express
Some thanks—' my friend, however, waved and said,
    'You go ahead.'

25    Once I had ventured in I felt betrayed,
    As I discerned
  A maze of winding walls that made
  Me dizzy, sad, until I turned
One corner and (in hope of what?) I saw
30    Another door.

Eager, I entered, to a gallery
    Closely comprised
  Of portals, each a vacancy
  For liberty. I realised
35  I'd never loved a room. It is the door
    That I adore.

**by Andrew Wynn Owen**

# Mixed Comprehension Questions — Text 1

Answer these questions about the text.
Circle the letter of the correct option for each question.

1. Why does the poet leave his room in lines 1-5?

    A He's easily distracted by interruptions to his work.

    B He wants to discover where the light is coming from.

    C He wants to stand up and stretch his legs.

    D He's eager to enjoy the bright sunlight outside.

2. Which of the following statements about the corridor is not true?

    A The corridor contains several doors with people's names above them.

    B The corridor extends a long way in front of the poet.

    C The corridor is well-known to the poet.

    D The poet accesses the corridor via a doorway.

3. Which of the following best describes how the poet feels
   about the room which has his name on the lintel?

    A Nervous but pleased

    B Delighted and cheerful

    C Calm but intrigued

    D Shocked but excited

4. What happens in lines 16-18?

    A The poet approaches the chair in the centre of the room.

    B The poet smiles at the contents of the room.

    C The chair swivels round of its own accord.

    D Someone in the chair turns to face the poet and greets him.

5. According to the poem, which of the following statements is true?

    A The poet walks through the arch without hesitation.

    B The poet feels indebted to his friend for showing him the arch.

    C The poet wants his friend to go through the arch before him.

    D The poet feels bad about leaving his friend behind.

/ 5

**Turn over for the next question**

Section Four — Comprehension

# Mixed Comprehension Questions — Text 1

Answer these questions about the text on page 32.
Circle the letter of the correct option for each question.

6.  The poet feels "betrayed" (line 25) because:

    A  he thought that the maze would be enjoyable but it makes him feel dizzy.

    B  his friend tricked him into entering a labyrinth he can't escape.

    C  his friend interrupted him abruptly when he attempted to thank him.

    D  he didn't expect to find a maze after going through the arch.

7.  How do you think the poet feels when he sees "Another door" (line 30)?

    A  His discouragement is replaced by hope.

    B  His dizziness is cured and he regains a sense of clarity.

    C  His sadness deepens into a sense of hopelessness.

    D  His expectations are finally confirmed.

8.  What does the poet mean when he says doors are a source of "liberty"?

    A  Doors are the gateway to happiness.

    B  Doors can lead to unpredictable destinations.

    C  Doors signify new beginnings.

    D  Doors offer people freedom and choice.

9.  What does the word "checked" (line 6) mean?

    A  Scrutinised

    B  Stopped

    C  Shortened

    D  Accelerated

10. What does the word "discerned" (line 26) mean?

    A  Came across

    B  Recognised

    C  Made out

    D  Glimpsed

/ 5

# Mixed Comprehension Questions — Text 2

> Read the passage below, then answer the questions that follow.

## An extract from 'Life of Pi'

In the morning I could not move. I was pinned by weakness to the tarpaulin. Even thinking was exhausting. I applied myself to thinking straight. At length, as slowly as a caravan of camels crossing a desert, some thoughts came together.

The day was like the previous one, warm and overcast, the clouds low, the breeze light.
5  That was one thought. The boat was rocking gently, that was another.

I thought of sustenance for the first time. I had not had a drop to drink or a bite to eat or a minute of sleep in three days. Finding this obvious explanation for my weakness brought me a little strength.

Richard Parker was still on board. In fact, he was directly beneath me. Incredible that
10 such a thing should need consent to be true, but it was only after much deliberation, upon assessing various mental items and points of view, that I concluded that it was not a dream or a delusion or a misplaced memory or a fancy or any other such falsity, but a solid, true thing witnessed while in a weakened, highly agitated state. The truth of it would be confirmed as soon as I felt well enough to investigate.

15    How I had failed to notice for two and a half days a 450-pound Bengal tiger in a lifeboat twenty-six feet long was a conundrum I would have to try to crack later, when I had more energy. The feat surely made Richard Parker the largest stowaway, proportionally speaking, in the history of navigation. From tip of nose to tip of tail he took up over a third of the length of the ship he was on.

20    You might think I lost all hope at that point. I did. And as a result I perked up and felt much better. We see that in sports all the time, don't we? The tennis challenger starts strong but soon loses confidence in his playing. The champion racks up the games. But in the final set, when the challenger has nothing left to lose, he becomes relaxed again, insouciant, daring. Suddenly he's playing like the devil and the champion must work hard to get those
25 last points. So it was with me. To cope with a hyena seemed remotely possible, but I was so obviously outmatched by Richard Parker that it wasn't even worth worrying about. With a tiger aboard, my life was over.

**by Yann Martel**

# Mixed Comprehension Questions — Text 2

> Answer these questions about the text on page 35.
> Circle the letter of the correct option for each question.

1.  Which of the following statements about the narrator is false?

    A  He has been on the lifeboat for at least two days.

    B  He is extremely hungry and thirsty.

    C  He is lying on a piece of tarpaulin.

    D  He has just woken from a night of fitful sleep.

2.  Which of the following best describes the conditions around the lifeboat?

    A  It is cold and cloudy, but there are only small waves.

    B  It is cloudy but not cold, and the waves are fairly small.

    C  It is very hot and the sea is mostly still.

    D  It is dark and overcast, and the waves are getting bigger.

3.  In what way is the tiger like a "stowaway" (line 17)?

    A  It boarded the lifeboat without the narrator's knowledge.

    B  It is trying its best to remain hidden from the narrator.

    C  It has remained in the lower section of the lifeboat.

    D  It is a serious threat to the narrator's life.

4.  Which of the following statements about the tiger must be true?

    A  It weighs over 450 pounds.

    B  It is over eight feet long.

    C  It is at the opposite end of the boat to the narrator.

    D  It got on the lifeboat after the narrator did.

5.  According to the passage, why might a "challenger" who is playing a "champion" (lines 21-22) perform better towards the end of a match?

    A  The challenger starts to believe they could actually win the match.

    B  The champion starts to get complacent after winning so many points.

    C  The challenger has started to work out the champion's weaknesses.

    D  The challenger feels less pressure as their defeat looks more likely.

/ 5

# Mixed Comprehension Questions — Text 2

Answer these questions about the text on page 35.
Circle the letter of the correct option for each question.

6.  Which of the following is not mentioned in the passage?

    **A**  What caused the narrator to notice the tiger

    **B**  What time of day it is

    **C**  What kind of tiger is on the boat

    **D**  What the weather was like on the previous day

7.  What does the narrator think is "Incredible" in lines 9-10?

    **A**  The fact that there is a tiger stowed away on the lifeboat.

    **B**  The fact that the tiger hasn't tried to kill him yet.

    **C**  The fact that he was unsure whether there was a tiger on board.

    **D**  The fact that the tiger hasn't moved for so long.

8.  What is ironic about the narrator's attitude in the final paragraph?

    **A**  He compares himself to a tennis player but he can't even move.

    **B**  He is so worried about the tiger that he forgets how tired he is.

    **C**  He starts to feel better when he realises he is doomed.

    **D**  He is worried about the hyena when the tiger is much more dangerous.

9.  What does the word "deliberation" (line 10) mean?

    **A**  Concern

    **B**  Contemplation

    **C**  Consultation

    **D**  Consolidation

10. What does the word "insouciant" (line 23) mean?

    **A**  Carefree

    **B**  Adept

    **C**  Shrewd

    **D**  Placid

/ 5

# Mixed Comprehension Questions — Text 3

Read the passage below, then answer the questions that follow.

## Snowdon Mountain Railway

On a clear, still summer's day, there are few vantage points in Britain more breathtaking than the summit of Snowdon, or Yr Wyddfa as it's known in Welsh. To the north, the rugged peaks of the Glyderau mountains stand majestic; to the south, the rest of Snowdonia National Park — visited annually by almost 4 million tourists — unfolds dramatically. Yet, access to

5 this sublime panorama is not exclusive to those with a propensity for hillwalking: the highest point in Wales can also be reached via train.

At a height of 1085 metres above sea level, Snowdon's summit can experience wind gusts of over 140 mph and temperatures as low as –20°C. Yet, the mountain's harsh climate was not enough to deter railway pioneer Sir Richard Moon. In 1869, he propounded the

10 idea of a train line linking it to the village of Llanberis on Snowdon's north-west flank. At this point, the summit was populated only by a cluster of wooden huts, most likely dating back to the 1820s. However, for a long time, Moon's plans were thwarted by the landowner, George Assheton-Smith, who worried that a railway would be an eyesore. Finally, Assheton-Smith had a change of heart, and after 25 years in limbo, the project could commence.

15 Work began in December of that year, and within 16 months all 7.5 km of track had been laid and the railway opened for business. To cope with the steep gradients, the engineers employed technology that had been used extensively in Swiss mountain railways. The track itself was designed in Switzerland, as were the five original steam trains. Over the years, new trains have been purchased: first, three more Swiss steam trains in the early

20 1920s, then four diesel locomotives between 1986 and 1992, and finally three diesel-electric railcars in 1995. Each train has its own name, some more conventional, like the steam train 'Snowdon', and others more whimsical, such as the diesel locomotive 'Yeti'.

The carriages have also undergone comprehensive development; for example, from 1947, enclosed roofs were steadily added to the original open-top carriages to better protect

25 passengers from the frequent inclement weather. At the summit, a striking granite building housing a bustling visitor centre and café opened in 2009. This superseded the unpopular concrete structure demolished three years earlier, which had itself been constructed in the 1930s to replace the wooden huts from the previous century.

Today, trains cart eager tourists to the summit as regularly as ever, and a ride on the

30 railway remains a popular choice for those seeking a different kind of mountain experience.

# Mixed Comprehension Questions — Text 3

Answer these questions about the text.
Circle the letter of the correct option for each question.

1.  According to the text, which of the following statements cannot be true?

    A  Snowdon Mountain Railway is the only mountain railway in Wales.

    B  Some of the original trains used on the railway are no longer in operation.

    C  'Yeti' was one of the railway's original trains.

    D  The railway was built with the landowner's consent.

2.  If you were travelling on the railway from Llanberis to the summit, what would be your general direction of travel?

    A  South-east to north-west

    B  South-west to north-east

    C  North-east to south-west

    D  North-west to south-east

3.  According to the text, which of these statements must be true?

    A  Nearly 4 million tourists visit Snowdon's summit every year.

    B  Snowdon is part of the Glyderau mountains.

    C  Snowdon is situated within a national park.

    D  There is no peak in Britain higher than 1085 metres above sea level.

4.  According to the text, which of the following best describes the weather on Snowdon's summit?

    A  It is often cold and windy, but sometimes more settled.

    B  It is very difficult to predict and therefore can be dangerous.

    C  It is usually icy and windy, even in the summer.

    D  It is typically clear and still in the summer, then cold and wet in the winter.

5.  In which of the following would a passenger on the Snowdon Mountain Railway have been able to ride in 1946?

    A  An open-top carriage pushed by a steam locomotive

    B  An open-top carriage pushed by a diesel locomotive

    C  An enclosed carriage pushed by a steam locomotive

    D  An enclosed carriage pushed by a diesel locomotive

/ 5

**Turn over for the next question**

# Mixed Comprehension Questions — Text 3

> Answer these questions about the text on page 38.
> Circle the letter of the correct option for each question.

6. According to the text, which of these statements must be true?

   A There were no buildings on Snowdon's summit in 1925.

   B The wooden huts that were on the summit in 1869 stood for less than a century.

   C The predecessor of the current summit building stood for over 65 years.

   D There has been some form of building on Snowdon's summit since the eighteenth century.

7. According to the text, which of these statements must be true?

   A The technology used for the Snowdon Mountain Railway was invented in Switzerland.

   B All the locomotives in operation on Snowdon in the 1930s were from Switzerland.

   C The Snowdon Mountain Railway was based on a mountain railway in Switzerland.

   D The Snowdon Mountain Railway was the world's first mountain railway outside Switzerland.

8. When did Snowdon Mountain Railway become operational?

   A December 1894

   B April 1895

   C December 1895

   D April 1896

9. What does the word "whimsical" (line 22) mean?

   A Unusual and fanciful

   B Memorable and striking

   C Bizarre and inexplicable

   D Interesting and evocative

10. What does the word "inclement" (line 25) mean?

    A Subject to sudden changes

    B Stormy and dangerous

    C Unpleasantly cold or wet

    D Extremely hot and humid

/ 5

# Mixed Comprehension Questions — Text 4

Read the passage below, then answer the questions that follow.

## An abridged extract from 'Northanger Abbey'

No one who had ever seen Catherine Morland in her infancy would have supposed her born to be an heroine. Her situation in life, the character of her father and mother, her own person and disposition, were all equally against her. Her father was a clergyman, without being neglected, or poor, and a very respectable man — and he had never been handsome.

5 He had a considerable independence besides two good livings* — and he was not in the least addicted to locking up his daughters. Her mother was a woman of useful plain sense, with a good temper, and, what is more remarkable, with a good constitution. She had three sons before Catherine was born; and instead of dying in bringing the latter into the world, as anybody might expect, she still lived on — lived to have six children more — to see them

10 growing up around her, and to enjoy excellent health herself. A family of ten children will be always called a fine family, but the Morlands had little other right to the word, for they were in general very plain, and Catherine, for many years of her life, as plain as any.

She had a thin awkward figure, a sallow skin without colour, dark lank hair, and strong features — so much for her person; and not less unpropitious* for heroism seemed her mind.

15 She was fond of all boy's plays, and greatly preferred cricket not merely to dolls, but to the more heroic enjoyments of infancy, nursing a dormouse, feeding a canary-bird, or watering a rose-bush. Indeed she had no taste for a garden; and if she gathered flowers at all, it was chiefly for the pleasure of mischief — at least so it was conjectured from her always preferring those which she was forbidden to take. Such were her propensities* — her abilities were

20 quite as extraordinary. She never could learn or understand anything before she was taught; and sometimes not even then, for she was often inattentive, and occasionally stupid. Her mother was three months in teaching her only to repeat the "Beggar's Petition"; and after all, her next sister, Sally, could say it better than she did. Not that Catherine was always stupid — by no means; she learnt the fable of "The Hare and Many Friends" as quickly as any girl in

25 England. Her mother wished her to learn music; and Catherine was sure she should like it, for she was very fond of tinkling the keys of the old forlorn spinnet; so, at eight years old she began. She learnt a year, and could not bear it; and Mrs. Morland, who did not insist on her daughters being accomplished in spite of incapacity or distaste, allowed her to leave off. The day which dismissed the music-master was one of the happiest of Catherine's life.

*livings — *incomes*        *unpropitious — *unfavourable*        **by Jane Austen**

*propensities — *tendencies*

# Mixed Comprehension Questions — Text 4

Answer these questions about the text on page 41.
Circle the letter of the correct option for each question.

1. Which of the following is not a reason why Catherine is an unlikely heroine?

   **A** Her parents' personalities
   **B** Her appearance
   **C** The size of her family
   **D** The way her mind works

2. Which of the following statements is true?

   **A** Catherine's music lessons ended after less than a year.
   **B** It was Catherine's idea to have music lessons.
   **C** Catherine tried playing an instrument prior to having lessons.
   **D** The music-master resigned from his position.

3. According to lines 15-19, which of the following adjectives best describes Catherine as a child?

   **A** Unconventional
   **B** Unpredictable
   **C** Impulsive
   **D** Malicious

4. According to the passage, which of the following statements about Catherine's father is false?

   **A** He is a religious man.
   **B** He is a controlling father.
   **C** He is financially stable.
   **D** He has a good reputation.

5. According to the passage, what is the most "remarkable" (line 7) thing about Mrs. Morland?

   **A** She is both friendly and level-headed at the same time.
   **B** She nearly died during Catherine's birth, but made a strong recovery.
   **C** Nobody expected her to have children, but she ended up having ten.
   **D** She was able to remain healthy after surviving multiple childbirths.

/ 5

# Mixed Comprehension Questions — Text 4

Answer these questions about the text on page 41.
Circle the letter of the correct option for each question.

6.  Which of the following statements about Catherine as a child is false?

    **A** She rarely gathered flowers.
    **B** She learnt better when she was working by herself.
    **C** She wasn't interested in taking care of animals.
    **D** She had very pale skin.

7.  According to the passage, Mrs. Morland "did not insist on her daughters being accomplished in spite of incapacity or distaste" (lines 27-28). What does this mean?

    **A** She didn't pressurise her children to share her interests, even when she felt disappointed.
    **B** She was often inclined to let her children give up activities that she didn't enjoy herself.
    **C** She didn't force her children to succeed at things they didn't like or weren't skilled at.
    **D** She refused to make her children participate in things they struggled to understand.

8.  Which of the following statements cannot be true?

    **A** Catherine has more brothers than sisters.
    **B** Catherine was the only family member to have music lessons.
    **C** Catherine is eight years older than her youngest sibling.
    **D** Catherine's sister Sally is older than her.

9.  What does the word "lank" (line 13) mean?

    **A** Thin
    **B** Coarse
    **C** Lifeless
    **D** Unkempt

10. What does the word "conjectured" (line 18) mean?

    **A** Contested
    **B** Supposed
    **C** Known
    **D** Demanded

/ 5

# Assessment Test 1

The rest of this book contains three assessment tests, which get progressively harder.

Allow 30 minutes to do each test and work as quickly and as carefully as you can.

You can print **multiple-choice answer sheets** for these questions from our website —
go to cgpbooks.co.uk/11plus/answer-sheets or scan the QR code on the right. If you'd
prefer to answer the questions on the page, just follow the instructions in the question.

Answer
Sheets

> Read this passage carefully and answer the questions that follow.

## The Shadow

A tranquil hue was settling over the valley as Liana made her way back to the watchtower.
Her hilltop village, once alive with neighbourly chatter, had been abandoned to the elements, the
cobblestone walkways scattered with items deemed unnecessary in an evacuation: a water bucket
here, a wooden broom there. Passing by, Liana didn't need the golden haze to enamour her to these
**5** seemingly mundane objects — the feeling of nostalgia was enough.

As she approached the watchtower's stony facade, she stopped. Its windows, set alight by the
sun, were glaring at something in the valley below. Following the tower's gaze, Liana scanned the
panoramic view, initially seeing nothing amiss, only the river sparkling in the distance and the grass
swaying gently in the breeze. But at the sight of the forest, with its trees' lengthening shadows, the
**10** hair on the back of her neck began to stand on end. The shadows were expanding too quickly
compared to the sun's slow descent, the darkness seeping out of the undergrowth at an alarming rate.
As a chill shot down her spine, she realised the dark mass wasn't a shadow at all, but an army.

Without hesitation, she charged over to the watchtower, clanging the alarm bell to alert the other
lookouts. The dreaded moment was upon them: the encroaching army would complete the climb
**15** from the valley to the village walls within the hour, forcing the lookouts to leave at once. Her stomach
churned at the thought of abandoning the place that had been her sanctuary for so long. But dwelling
on that now wouldn't do — she and her companions could only fulfil their duty and flee with the news
to where the queen's army was stationed, carrying nothing but the hope that one day they might return.

> Answer these questions about the text that you've just read.
> Circle the letter of the correct answer.

1. At what time of day does the story take place?

   **A** Morning
   **B** Midday
   **C** Evening
   **D** Night-time

2. Why is Liana in the abandoned village?

   **A** She is visiting the place where she grew up.
   **B** She is working there as a lookout.
   **C** She is cleaning up the mess left behind.
   **D** She is helping to build the watchtower.

/ 2

3.  According to the passage, what are the lookouts planning to do once they leave the village?

    **A**  Notify their queen that she needs to form an army and fight back.
    **B**  Tell people in neighbouring villages to run and hide.
    **C**  Get as far away from the oncoming army as possible.
    **D**  Warn their own army that another army is approaching.

4.  Which word best describes how Liana reacts when she sees the army?

    **A**  Stealthily
    **B**  Nonchalantly
    **C**  Erratically
    **D**  Decisively

5.  How does Liana feel as she walks through the village?

    **A**  She is worried about the village being attacked.
    **B**  She feels a strong personal attachment to the village.
    **C**  She is impressed by how beautiful the village is.
    **D**  She is saddened by the abandoned objects on the streets.

6.  How does Liana work out that the dark mass isn't actually a shadow?

    **A**  The dark mass contains colours other than black and grey.
    **B**  The speed at which the dark mass grows is too fast.
    **C**  The outline of the dark mass doesn't match the outline of the trees.
    **D**  The dark mass is growing in a different direction to the trees' shadows.

7.  Which of the following statements is true?

    **A**  The village's former inhabitants led solitary lives.
    **B**  Liana knows she'll never return to the village.
    **C**  The lookouts have been expecting an army to arrive.
    **D**  Liana has time to collect her belongings before leaving.

8.  Which of the following statements is false?

    **A**  Liana's village is located in a valley.
    **B**  The forest is downhill from the village.
    **C**  The river is a long way from the watchtower.
    **D**  The watchtower's windows are reflecting the sun.

9.  Which of the following isn't mentioned in the passage?

    **A**  How Liana signals to the lookouts that an army is coming
    **B**  What the temperature is like outside
    **C**  What the watchtower is made out of
    **D**  How soon the approaching army will arrive

/ 7

**Carry on to the next question → →**

10. What is meant by the word "hue" (line 1)?

    **A**  Sound
    **B**  Colour
    **C**  Light
    **D**  Mood

11. What is meant by the word "mundane" (line 5)?

    **A**  Unremarkable
    **B**  Unused
    **C**  Unnecessary
    **D**  Unoriginal

12. What is meant by the word "panoramic" (line 8)?

    **A**  Spectacular
    **B**  Clear
    **C**  Grand
    **D**  Wide

13. What is meant by the phrase "abandoned to the elements" (lines 2)?

    **A**  Damaged by extreme weather
    **B**  Given up to other people
    **C**  Left to the mercy of the weather
    **D**  Deserted by all but a few people

14. What is meant by the phrase "dwelling on that now wouldn't do" (line 17)?

    **A**  Nothing could be done to change the situation.
    **B**  There were no other options.
    **C**  Thinking about it wouldn't help.
    **D**  Living there wasn't possible anymore.

/ 5

Three of the words in each list are linked.  Mark the word that is not related to these three.

15. pronounce    stress    emphasise    underline

16. rectify    soothe    remedy    amend

17. blueprint    convention    directions    recipe

18. solder    tether    fuse    weld

19. adroit    deft    skilled    efficient

20. foundation    structure    bedrock    bottom

21. chorus    troupe    troubadour    ensemble

22. coil    curve    spiral    whorl

23. headland    cove    peninsula    promontory

/ 9

Choose the phrase that best fits each gap in the passage below.

Reports that a mythical beast resides in the town of Shorly Knott

24. **A** have recently come to light
**B** are yet to be confirmed
**C** may have some basis in fact
**D** have existed for centuries

,

despite locals' insistence as to their truth.

25. **A** Though the tale remains unpopular
**B** Although initial sightings were ignored
**C** After the rumour spread nationwide
**D** In addition to the townsfolk

, visitors from

near and far arrived in droves.  However, visitors left with

26. **A** few worries
**B** conflicting accounts
**C** feelings of suspense
**D** overactive imaginations

, as locals'

descriptions of the beast differed.  This has led to speculation that the reports are part of a clever bid to

attract tourists, since local tourism has been suffering

27. **A** to a lesser extent
**B** since the first sighting
**C** as a consequence
**D** in recent years

.

/ 4

Look at the definition on the left.  Mark the word on the right that best matches the definition.

**Example: to long for**     love   <u>yearn</u>   urge   incline

28. **a person of lower rank**          minor    subordinate    adherent    sidekick

29. **to request something be made**   obtain   commission   proclaim   delegate

30. **to let oneself enjoy something**  surrender   revel   savour   indulge

31. **extremely terrible**              profound   lethal   abysmal   formidable

32. **agreement within a group**        concession   solidarity   affinity   acceptance

33. **aware of one's surroundings**     intuitive   endowed   competent   conscious

34. **willing to talk to people**       communicative   articulate   tedious   eloquent

35. **confident and happy**             hysterical   earnest   emphatic   buoyant

36. **to make a situation worse**       hamper   stimulate   exacerbate   incense

37. **a deviation from normality**      rotation   vice   aberration   disobedience

/ 10

**Carry on to the next question → →**

Assessment Test 1

Each sentence contains a spelling mistake. Circle the
letter beneath the group of words with the mistake.

38. The famous musician said it had been a priviledge to perform for the audience.

         **A**          **B**         **C**         **D**

39. There's a noticable difference in the twins' behaviour, despite their identical appearance.

         **A**          **B**         **C**         **D**

40. Tiptoeing through the eerie mansion, Dylan felt an ominous presense behind him.

         **A**          **B**         **C**         **D**

41. I was advised to research the spiders that inhabit the rainforest, but I decided ignorence is bliss.

         **A**          **B**         **C**         **D**

42. The inhabitants of the ancient settlement were skilfull at carving miniature ornaments.

         **A**          **B**         **C**         **D**

43. The explorers rangled with the prospect of venturing further into the treacherous jungle.

         **A**          **B**         **C**         **D**    / 6

---

Mark the word in the set of brackets that completes the sentence in the most sensible way.

**Example: Leopard** is to **spot** as **zebra** is to (<u>stripe</u>  leap  see  pattern).

44. **Slogan** is to **catchphrase** as **perimeter** is to (line  outline  extremity  radius).

45. **Swan** is to (fledgling  cygnet  gosling  eaglet) as **kangaroo** is to **joey**.

46. **Rule** is to (follow  enforce  punishment  regulation) as **guideline** is to **recommendation**.

47. **Manual** is to **instructions** as (anthology  inventory  register  dictionary) is to **names**.

48. **Rickety** is to (organised  stable  common  unbroken) as **amateur** is to **specialist**.

49. (Sanction  Yield  Recline  Collapse) is to **surrender** as **respire** is to **breathe**.

50. **Cumbersome** is to **convenient** as **obscure** is to (logical  apparent  secure  understood).

51. **Ship** is to (mast  deck  sails  bow) as **plane** is to **nose**.

52. **Neuroscientist** is to **brain** as **nutritionist** is to (diet  behaviour  body  stomach).

53. **Everlasting** is to **eternal** as **flawless** is to (revered  preeminent  consecrated  unblemished).

54. **Condemnation** is to (ovation  gratitude  adulation  recognition) as **learned** is to **instinctive**.

55. **Absolve** is to (suspect  frame  discount  convict) as **advantage** is to **hindrance**.

56. (Turquoise  Alabaster  Jade  Obsidian) is to **black** as **mauve** is to **purple**.

/ 13

Complete the word on the right so that it means the same, or nearly the same, as the word on the left.

**Example: stone** [b][o][u][l][d][e][r]

57. **mock** [ ][ ][a][s][ ]

58. **deal** [ ][r][a][ ][ ][c][t][ ][ ][n]

59. **gloomy** [ ][e][ ][ ][n][c][ ][o][ ][y]

60. **widespread** [ ][i][f][ ]

61. **wealthy** [ ][f][ ][l][u][ ][n][ ]

62. **hunt** [ ][o][ ][a][g][ ]

63. **guess** [ ][p][ ][c][ ][l][ ][ ][e]

64. **unfashionable** [ ][u][d][ ][t][e][ ]

65. **debatable** [u][ ][c][ ][ ][t][a][ ][ ]

66. **apologetic** [ ][ ][g][ ][e][ ][f][ ][l]

67. **mysterious** [ ][r][y][ ][t][i][ ]

68. **loathed** [a][ ][h][ ][r][ ][ ][d]

( / 12 )

(Total [ / 68])

**End of Test**

Assessment Test 1

# Assessment Test 2

Allow 30 minutes to do this test and work as quickly and as carefully as you can.

You can print **multiple-choice answer sheets** for these questions from our website —
go to cgpbooks.co.uk/11plus/answer-sheets or scan the QR code on the right. If you'd
prefer to answer the questions on the page, just follow the instructions in the question.

Read this passage carefully and answer the questions that follow.

## An abridged extract from 'The Woman in White'

The moon was full and broad in the dark blue starless sky, and the broken ground of the heath
looked wild enough in the mysterious light to be hundreds of miles away from the great city that lay
beneath it. The idea of descending any sooner than I could help into the heat and gloom of London
repelled me. The prospect of going to bed in my airless chambers, and the prospect of gradual

5   suffocation, seemed, in my present restless frame of mind and body, to be one and the same thing.
I determined to stroll home in the purer air by the most roundabout way I could take; to follow the
white winding paths across the lonely heath; and to approach London through its most open suburb
by striking into the Finchley Road, and so getting back, in the cool of the new morning, by the western
side of the Regent's Park.

10   I wound my way down slowly over the heath, enjoying the divine stillness of the scene, and
admiring the soft alternations of light and shade as they followed each other over the broken ground on
every side of me. So long as I was proceeding through this first and prettiest part of my night walk my
mind remained open to the impressions produced by the view; and I thought but little on any subject.

When I had left the heath, I arrived at that particular point of my walk where four roads met —
15   the road to Hampstead, along which I had returned, the road to Finchley, the road to West End, and
the road back to London. I had mechanically turned in this latter direction, and was strolling along the
lonely high-road when, in one moment, every drop of blood in my body was brought to a stop by the
touch of a hand laid lightly and suddenly on my shoulder from behind me.

I turned on the instant, with my fingers tightening round the handle of my stick.

20   There, in the middle of the broad bright high-road — there, as if it had that moment sprung out
of the earth or dropped from the heaven — stood the figure of a solitary woman, dressed from head
to foot in white garments, her face bent in grave inquiry on mine, her hand pointing to the dark cloud
over London, as I faced her.

**by Wilkie Collins**

Answer these questions about the text that you've just read.
Circle the letter of the correct answer.

1.   Why is the narrator reluctant to go home and sleep immediately?

    **A**  He doesn't feel tired.
    **B**  He finds his lodgings too stuffy.
    **C**  His room lets in too much light.
    **D**  He is in the mood for exploring the heath.

/ 1

2. Which of the following best describes the narrator's attitude to the heath and London?

    **A** He thinks the heath is comforting and safe, whereas London is menacing and dangerous.
    **B** He thinks the heath is quiet and empty, whereas London is loud and bustling.
    **C** He thinks the heath is mysterious and exciting, whereas London is boring and familiar.
    **D** He thinks the heath is tranquil and appealing, whereas London is dark and oppressive.

3. Which of the following best describes the route the narrator intends to take home?

    **A** He plans to cross a roundabout and head to the heath before going to Finchley.
    **B** He plans to go straight across the heath before entering London via Regent's Park.
    **C** He plans to meander across the heath before entering London via Finchley Road.
    **D** He plans to stroll around the heath before heading directly to London on the high-road.

4. "my mind remained open to the impressions produced by the view; and I thought but little on any subject" (lines 12-13). This suggests that the narrator:

    **A** isn't focusing on anything in particular, except for admiring the scenery.
    **B** isn't thinking about much and doesn't notice the beauty of his surroundings.
    **C** is absent-mindedly watching shadows moving across the heath.
    **D** is concentrating so hard on the view that he cannot think about anything else.

5. Which of the following statements about the mysterious woman is not true?

    **A** She is wearing only white clothes.
    **B** She appears on the road very suddenly.
    **C** She is staring at London in the distance.
    **D** She has a serious expression on her face.

6. Why does the narrator take the road back to London when he is at the crossroads?

    **A** He thinks it will be the quietest route.
    **B** He thinks it is the road to Finchley.
    **C** He isn't familiar with the other roads.
    **D** He acts on instinct.

7. How does the narrator react when the woman taps his shoulder?

    **A** He is irritated at being shaken out of his thoughts.
    **B** He is filled with dread but prepared to defend himself.
    **C** He is terrified and is frozen to the spot.
    **D** He is shocked and prepares to flee.

8. According to the text, why does the heath seem like it is "hundreds of miles away from" London (line 2)?

    **A** London is situated far below the heath.
    **B** The heath looks very different to London.
    **C** The heath is incredibly vast.
    **D** The darkness makes it hard to judge the distance.

/ 7

9. What is meant by the word "repelled" (line 4)?

   **A** Remanded
   **B** Rebuked
   **C** Repulsed
   **D** Reviled

10. What is meant by the word "alternations" (line 11)?

   **A** Movements
   **B** Patterns
   **C** Reflections
   **D** Interchanges

/ 2

---

Complete the word on the right so that it means the opposite, or nearly the opposite, of the word on the left.

**Example: depart** r e m a i n

11. **peaceful** ☐ ☐ ☐ b ☐ l e n ☐

12. **shortcoming** ☐ ☐ r t ☐ e

13. **unite** ☐ u ☐ t u ☐ e

14. **conclusion** i ☐ c e ☐ t ☐ o ☐

15. **heed** ☐ i s ☐ e ☐ a r ☐

16. **nurture** ☐ e ☐ l ☐ c t

17. **impulsive** c ☐ ☐ ☐ ☐ o u s

18. **discourage** ☐ e ☐ s u a ☐ ☐

19. **nondescript** ☐ t r ☐ ☐ i n ☐

20. **insolent** c ☐ ☐ r ☐ e ☐ u ☐

21. **unleash** s ☐ ☐ ☐ r e ☐ s

22. **inarticulate** ☐ l o ☐ u e ☐ ☐

23. **neutral** ☐ r ☐ j u ☐ ☐ c e ☐

24. **spartan** ☐ r n ☐ t ☐

25. **disrespectful** ☐ e f ☐ ☐ e n t ☐ a ☐

/ 15

> Read this passage carefully and answer the questions that follow.

# An adapted extract from 'The Heart of Hyacinth'

It was the season of Seed Rain; the country was green and fragrant. The villagers sat at their thresholds, some indolently lounging in the open, unmindful or enjoying the seething rain, an antidote for the heat. Children were climbing the trees. One small boy had climbed to the tip of a bamboo, swaying with the shakings of the slender tree, and the motion of those below him — far below him.

5 It was not often that the son of Madame Aoi was permitted such absolute freedom. It was only upon those occasions when Komazawa, momentarily blind to the reproach of his mother's sad eyes, thrust away the bonds which chained him to their quiet household. At the tip of this perilous bamboo he was quite beyond the reach of Madame Aoi and her servant, Mumè. But even in his lofty position he kept his eyes from his mother. His feet clung to the tree only as his hands were covering his ears.

10 The neighbours' children played in groups, and Komazawa from his perch watched them with the same ardent wistfulness with which he habitually regarded them from the door of his little isolated home.

Mumè, tired of her position in the rain, for the bamboo gave but scant shelter, shook the tree angrily.

"Do not so," entreated the gentle Aoi. "See how the tree bends. Take care lest it become angry with us and vent its vengeance upon my son. Ah, Koma, Koma, son, do pray come down."

**by Onoto Watanna**

> Answer these questions about the text that you've just read.
> Circle the letter of the correct answer.

26. According to the text, which of the following statements cannot be true?

   **A**  The village is located in a rural area.
   **B**  The area is experiencing a wet season.
   **C**  The village's surroundings are lush and fertile.
   **D**  The villagers are all finding the weather uncomfortable.

27. According to the text, which of the following statements cannot be true?

   **A**  Komazawa lives in quite a strict household.
   **B**  Madame Aoi and Komazawa have a tense relationship.
   **C**  Komazawa normally climbs trees with other children.
   **D**  Madame Aoi and Mumè do not agree on much.

28. Which of the following is not mentioned in the text?

   **A**  How Komazawa gripped the tree
   **B**  How long Komazawa had been up the tree
   **C**  How far up the tree Komazawa had climbed
   **D**  The type of tree Komazawa climbed

29. Why does Madame Aoi ask Mumè not to shake the tree?

   **A**  She is nervous that Mumè will damage their precious tree.
   **B**  She thinks Komazawa is about to fall from the tree.
   **C**  She thinks that the act might make Komazawa cross with them.
   **D**  She is worried that the tree might break and injure Komazawa in the process.

( / 4 )

**Carry on to the next question → →**

Assessment Test 2

Circle the letters which correspond to the correct words to complete the passage below.

When

30.
**A** the
**B** most
**C** ever
**D** few

people hear the words 'black hole', they

31.
**A** devise
**B** believe
**C** assume
**D** visualise

a gigantic pit of darkness,

swirling

32.
**A** among
**B** through
**C** by
**D** outer

space and sucking in everything around it.  The

33.
**A** narrative
**B** reality
**C** rationale
**D** authenticity

,

however, is more

34.
**A** complicated
**B** intelligible
**C** comparable
**D** physical

and mysterious.  Black holes do have an

35.
**A** absolutely
**B** indistinctly
**C** optionally
**D** exceedingly

strong gravitational pull — gravity pulls so powerfully towards the centre

36.
**A** during
**B** from
**C** of
**D** around

a black hole

that

37.
**A** no
**B** many
**C** only
**D** even

light cannot escape.  For this reason, black holes are

38.
**A** invisible
**B** misunderstood
**C** observable
**D** illusory

; scientists

are only able to

39.
**A** regulate
**B** measure
**C** detect
**D** quantify

their existence by observing their effect on

40.
**A** nearby
**B** another
**C** closer
**D** adjoining

stars.  Thankfully, it

41.
**A** may
**B** might
**C** could
**D** would

seem that Earth is

42.
**A** expected
**B** never
**C** unlikely
**D** vulnerable

to be sucked into a black hole

anytime soon.

43.
**A** According
**B** Similar
**C** Contrary
**D** Due

to popular belief, black holes are not magnets that gradually suck

everything into them;

44.
**A** instead
**B** nevertheless
**C** additionally
**D** meanwhile

, they only affect objects within a

45.
**A** limitless
**B** random
**C** certain
**D** vast

area,

46.
**A** accredited
**B** referred
**C** attributed
**D** hinted

to as their "radius of influence".  The nearest

47.
**A** artificial
**B** realistic
**C** truthful
**D** confirmed

black hole to Earth is

48.
**A** almost
**B** just
**C** clearly
**D** estimated

5000 light-years away — much too far to

49.
**A** cause
**B** provoke
**C** perturb
**D** raise

us any concern.

/ 20

In each question below, the words can be rearranged to form a sentence. One word doesn't fit in the sentence. Mark the word that doesn't fit.

**Example:** playing <u>very</u> Katya hockey likes

50. nearly hour the for enter long queued they museum an to

51. my am a Cornwall going to grandmother I planning with trip

52. on been of summers record the this has hottest weather one

53. woman some son while the called news immediately her with

54. cooked of powerful with in a being filled curry the was room aroma

/ 5

---

Find the word that means the same, or nearly the same, as the word on the left.

**Example:** **frown**   smirk   wince   <u>scowl</u>   ridicule

55. **lobby**         alcove   foyer   booth   chest

56. **pristine**      lavish   exquisite   immaculate   expressive

57. **reject**        disdain   rebuff   rankle   affront

58. **design**        appoint   insinuate   simulate   devise

59. **bold**          ludicrous   adamant   predisposed   audacious

60. **incidental**    monumental   negligible   unintentional   inexpensive

61. **determined**    tenacious   forthright   bestial   onerous

62. **slink**         skulk   slacken   scuttle   saunter

63. **rebellion**     regression   mutiny   strike   sabotage

64. **violate**       incarcerate   desecrate   infuriate   decimate

65. **deliverance**   immunity   transferral   revelation   salvation

66. **exclude**       liberate   supplant   ostracise   reprimand

67. **disobedient**   insubordinate   cumbersome   insufficient   prodigal

68. **fawning**       self-indulgent   obsequious   hypocritical   unworldly

/ 14

Total   / 68

**End of Test**

Assessment Test 2

# Assessment Test 3

Allow 30 minutes to do this test and work as quickly and as carefully as you can.

You can print **multiple-choice answer sheets** for these questions from our website — go to cgpbooks.co.uk/11plus/answer-sheets or scan the QR code on the right. If you'd prefer to answer the questions on the page, just follow the instructions in the question.

Answer Sheets

Read this poem carefully and answer the questions that follow.

## The Vagabonds

What saw you in your flight to-day,
Crows, awinging your homeward way?

Went you far in carrion quest,
Crows, that worry the sunless west?

5   Thieves and villains, you shameless things!
Black your record as black your wings.

Tell me, birds of the inky hue,
Plunderous rogues — today have you

Seen with mischievous, prying eyes
10  Lands where earlier suns arise?

Saw you a lazy beck between
Trees that shadow its breast in green,

Teased by obstinate stones that lie
Crossing the current tauntingly?

15  Fields abloom on the farther side
With purpling clover lying wide —

Saw you there as you circled by,
Vale-environed a cottage lie,

Girt* about with emerald bands,
20  Nestling down in its meadow lands?

Saw you this on your thieving raids?
Speak — you rascally renegades!

Thieved you also away from me
Olden scenes that I long to see?

25  If, O! crows, you have flown since morn
Over the place where I was born,

Forget will I, how black you were
Since dawn, in feather and character;

Absolve will I, your vagrant band
30  Ere* you enter your slumberland.

**by E. Pauline Johnson**

*Girt — *encircled*        *Ere — *before*

Answer these questions about the text that you've just read.
Circle the letter of the correct answer.

1.   Which of the following best describes the poet's attitude to the crows?

   **A**   She thinks they are dangerous and despicable.
   **B**   She thinks they are secretive and mysterious.
   **C**   She thinks they are wicked and sly.
   **D**   She thinks they are powerful and magical.

/ 1

2. According to the poem, what were the crows searching for on their flight?

   **A**  Trees to shelter in
   **B**  A cottage in a vale
   **C**  Faraway lands
   **D**  Dead animals

3. The poet describes the crows as "birds of the inky hue" (line 7).  This means that:

   **A**  they have sinister intentions.
   **B**  they cannot be seen in the dark.
   **C**  they have done evil things.
   **D**  their feathers are black.

4. Which of the following statements about the beck is not true?

   **A**  There are fields of flowers on one side of it.
   **B**  The water flows rapidly.
   **C**  It is shaded.
   **D**  There are trees growing on its banks.

5. Which of the following statements about the cottage must be true?

   **A**  It is next to a purple meadow.
   **B**  It looks as though its walls are encrusted with gems.
   **C**  It is where the poet's parents live.
   **D**  It is in a valley full of green fields.

6. The poet asks whether the crows have seen "Lands where earlier suns arise" (line 10).
   This suggests the poet thinks:

   **A**  the crows have the power to see into the past.
   **B**  the crows might have flown to distant places.
   **C**  the crows have been alive for a very long time.
   **D**  the crows might have flown high in the sky to witness the sunrise.

7. The poet offers to forgive the crows if they:

   **A**  stop stealing from her.
   **B**  stop flying and go to sleep.
   **C**  can tell her about somewhere from her past.
   **D**  share with her all their secrets.

8. The beck is described as being "Teased by obstinate stones that lie / Crossing the current
   tauntingly" (lines 13-14).  What does this mean?

   **A**  The stones are being swept along by the current but won't sink.
   **B**  The stones are teetering on the edge of the beck and could fall in at any moment.
   **C**  The stones have blocked the beck's passage, and it cannot keep flowing.
   **D**  The stones are in the middle of the beck, but the current cannot move them.

/ 7

**Carry on to the next question → →**

Assessment Test 3

9. What is meant by the word "Plunderous" (line 8)?

    **A** Destructive
    **B** Pilfering
    **C** Incorrigible
    **D** Pugnacious

10. What is meant by the word "vagrant" (line 29)?

    **A** Nomadic
    **B** Motley
    **C** Infamous
    **D** Formidable

( / 2 )

---

> Fill in the missing letters to complete the words in the following passage.

11. Known as the home of British motor racing, Silverstone is ☐ n d o ☐ ☐ ☐ e ☐ l y

12. the most famous race track in the country. Its ☐ ☐ i g ☐ ☐ ☐ s can be traced back to the

13. late 1940s, when Britain was still recovering from the ☐ ☐ r m ☐ ☐ ☐ l of World War II.

14. At this time, motor racing was steadily growing in ☐ o ☐ ☐ l ☐ r i t ☐ .

15. The story goes that a group of racing ☐ n ☐ h ☐ ☐ i a ☐ ☐ s were gathered in

16. a Worcestershire pub in September 1947, discussing ☐ o t e ☐ ☐ i ☐ l venues for

17. future races, when one of them mentioned a d ☐ s ☐ ☐ ☐ d airfield near his home.

18. The next day, the group set off for Silverstone airfield, where they ☐ t a ☐ ☐ d a race.

19. Although this unofficial race was not without incident, it was d ☐ e ☐ ☐ d a success.

20. Word spread, and, in 1948, the Royal Automobile Club ☐ ☐ a n ☐ ☐ o r ☐ ☐ d

21. the airfield into a ☐ e g ☐ t ☐ m ☐ ☐ e race track. In its early years, the circuit

22. hosted several ☐ r o ☐ ☐ n e n ☐ races, including the 1948 British Grand Prix and

23. the m ☐ ☐ d ☐ n Formula One World Championship race two years later. To this day,

24. Silverstone remains a popular ☐ i ☐ t ☐ r e in the Formula One calendar, where it has

25. a ☐ ☐ p ☐ ☐ a t i ☐ ☐ for being one of the fastest tracks.

( / 15 )

Read this passage carefully and answer the questions that follow.

# The Polar Bear Capital of the World

Travel 1000 km north by train from Winnipeg and you will arrive at the town of Churchill, which, despite its oppressive climate, diminutive size and extreme remoteness, is one of Canada's leading tourist destinations.  The reason?  Polar bears.  Churchill sits on a polar bear migration path: the bears pass through in autumn en route to the sea ice of the Hudson Bay, where they spend the winter
5   hunting seals.  Every year, during this six-week "Bear Season", around 10 000 tourists flock to the town, roughly ten times the number of locals, each of them hoping to glimpse the elusive carnivores.

Although the polar bears unquestionably take centre stage, there are other reasons to visit Churchill: in the summer, boats ferry tourists around the Hudson Bay in search of migrating beluga whales, while Churchill's northerly latitude makes it ideal for viewing the northern lights, which are
10   visible up to 300 nights every year, most strikingly so in the winter months.

Despite the thriving tourist industry, the town's permanent population has plummeted since its peak of nearly 2000 in the 1960s.  Transport problems have accelerated this slide; in 2017, following sustained adverse weather, Churchill's railway was rendered inoperable for almost 18 months, severing those who could not afford air fares from the outside world.  The government has since
15   pledged funds to improve local infrastructure — it is hoped this will improve life for the remaining residents, who are at risk of being outnumbered by the polar bears that make the town so famous.

Answer these questions about the text that you've just read.
Circle the letter of the correct answer.

26. Which of the following is not a reason why Churchill's popularity with tourists is surprising?

   **A**   The weather in Churchill is very harsh.
   **B**   Churchill is far away from other human settlements.
   **C**   Churchill sits on a polar bear migration path.
   **D**   The town of Churchill is very small.

27. According to the text, which of the following statements cannot be true?

   **A**   It is possible to see the northern lights in Churchill during the summer.
   **B**   Polar bears can sometimes be seen near Churchill in the spring.
   **C**   In summer, most tourists visit Churchill to see beluga whales.
   **D**   The Hudson Bay remains frozen all year round.

28. According to the text, which of the following statements must be true?

   **A**   On any given day in "Bear Season", tourists outnumber Churchill residents by ten to one.
   **B**   The population of Churchill has fallen by approximately 50% since its peak.
   **C**   Churchill's population has been steadily decreasing since 1965.
   **D**   Churchill currently has a population of just over 1000 people.

29. According to the text, which of the following statements must be true?

   **A**   Churchill is not connected to the rest of Canada by road.
   **B**   The tourist industry was unaffected by the problems with the railway.
   **C**   Churchill was inaccessible via train for all of 2018.
   **D**   Churchill's railway line was entirely rebuilt in the late 2010s.

/ 4

**Carry on to the next question → →**

Find the word that means the opposite, or nearly the opposite, of the word on the left.

**Example: tighten**     consolidate   emancipate   unleash   <u>slacken</u>

30. **urban**           barren   secluded   antiquated   pastoral

31. **validate**        deplore   debunk   denounce   debate

32. **dissuade**        acclaim   cajole   bolster   oblige

33. **prosper**         waver   devastate   flounder   wilt

34. **logical**         irrational   injurious   spurious   equivocal

35. **belittle**        reassure   alleviate   antagonise   extol

36. **overt**           surreptitious   lumbering   uncouth   tenuous

37. **unconvincing**    conscientious   enlightening   cogent   rational

38. **inconstant**      fugitive   altruistic   immutable   provident

39. **sophisticated**   placid   staid   farcical   gauche

/ 10

Mark the word outside the brackets that has a similar meaning to the words in both sets of brackets.

**Example:** (clever   intelligent)   (intense   vivid)       quick   <u>bright</u>   shiny   smart

40. (maintain   assert)     (battle   compete)       aver   advocate   engage   contend

41. (clatter   clack)       (unnerve   distress)     shatter   fluster   rattle   maunder

42. (nestle   nurse)        (birthplace   origin)    cradle   fount   spring   rock

43. (charter   grant)       (flagrant   conspicuous)  manifest   evident   patent   covenant

44. (yield   concede)       (postpone   delay)       acquiesce   adjourn   impede   defer

45. (desert   forsake)      (recklessness   freedom)  abandon   maroon   abjure   neglect

46. (licence   clearance)   (necessitate   require)  sanction   warrant   demand   permit

47. (coincide   correlate)  (communicate   write)    contact   conform   complement   correspond

48. (finish   complete)     (accomplished   skilled)  effectuate   clinch   consummate   master

49. (cliff   crag)          (pretend   feign)        dupe   bluff   scarp   profess

/ 10

> Three of the words in each list are linked.  Mark the word that is not related to these three.
>
> **Example:**  raincoat   umbrella   <u>parasol</u>   anorak

50. cathedral   palace   temple   mosque

51. scythe   axe   chainsaw   secateurs

52. deplorable   grievous   heinous   witless

53. florin   medallion   shilling   farthing

54. stethoscope   periscope   microscope   telescope

55. heartburn   epidemic   colic   flu

56. propagate   balloon   proliferate   burgeon

57. harbinger   portend   herald   precursor

58. smirk   glower   pout   simper

( / 9 )

> Rearrange the letters in capitals to spell a word that completes the sentence in a sensible way.
>
> **Example:**   Em needed **GERSYRU** after breaking her leg.   ( <u>surgery</u> )

59. The house was surrounded by gently **TNAGLUDNUI** hills.   _____

60. Watch out — the chemical gives off **OIXUNSO** fumes.   _____

61. Our **IPECNSREETS** finally paid off and we won the game.   _____

62. There was a **SUIOTRO** atmosphere at the hockey match.   _____

63. He ran his grimy fingers through his **EDSLHEIEDLV** hair.   _____

64. We tried to console her but she was **GSUTIRHDAT**.   _____

65. Her research casts doubt on the **RTIEYVCA** of your claims.   _____

66. Polly approached the angry bull with **ETNDTPAIRIO**.   _____

67. Madhi **ESREHISL** any opportunity to go stargazing.   _____

68. The volcano's eruption was a truly **YCAIMALCCST** event.   _____

( / 10 )

( Total   / 68 )

**End of Test**

Assessment Test 3

# Glossary

| | |
|---|---|
| adjective | A word that describes a noun, e.g. 'delightful evening', 'grassy meadow'. |
| adverb | A word that describes a verb or an adjective, which often ends with the suffix '-ly', e.g. 'She spoke quietly.', 'He sang beautifully.' |
| antonym | A word that has the opposite meaning to another word, e.g. the antonym of 'big' is 'small'. |
| conjunction | A word that joins two clauses, e.g. 'and', 'or'. |
| consonants | The 21 letters of the alphabet that aren't vowels. |
| fiction | Text that has been made up by the author, about imaginary people and events. |
| homographs | Words that are spelt the same but have different meanings, e.g. 'I go to the park.' and 'I park my car.' |
| homophones | Words that sound the same, but mean different things, e.g. 'right' and 'write'. |
| imagery | Language that creates a vivid picture in the reader's mind. |
| metaphor | A way of describing something by saying that it is something else, e.g. 'The clouds were a woolly blanket.' |
| multiple choice | A type of 11+ question that gives you answers to choose from. |
| non-fiction | Text that is about facts and real people and events. |
| noun | A word that names something, e.g. 'Kaya', 'river', 'joy', 'belief'. |
| personification | A way of describing something by giving it human feelings and characteristics, e.g. 'The daffodils nodded their heads contentedly in the breeze.' |
| prefix | Letters that can be put in front of a word to change its meaning, e.g. 'un-' can be added to 'pack' to make 'unpack'. |
| pronoun | Words that can be used instead of nouns, e.g. 'I', 'you', 'he', 'it'. |
| simile | A way of describing something by comparing it to something else, e.g. 'Archie weaved through the crowds like a needle and thread.' |
| subject | The person or thing doing the action of a verb, e.g. 'Flo smiled.', 'The cat purred.' |
| suffix | Letters that can be put after a word to change its meaning, e.g. '-er' can be added to the end of 'dry' to make 'dryer'. |
| synonym | A word with a similar meaning to another word, e.g. 'scared' is a synonym of 'afraid'. |
| verb | An action or doing word, e.g. 'dance', 'sneeze', 'agree', or a being word, e.g. 'is'. |
| vowels | The letters 'a', 'e', 'i', 'o' and 'u'. |

# Answers

## Section One — Making Words

### Page 2 — Anagrams

1) **BIOLOGY** — BIOLOGY is the only correctly spelled word that matches the definition.

2) **SUMMARY** — SUMMARY is the only correctly spelled word that matches the definition.

3) **EMBRACE** — EMBRACE is the only correctly spelled word that matches the definition.

4) **FINANCIAL** — FINANCIAL is the only correctly spelled word that matches the definition.

5) **SCOLD** — SCOLD is the only correctly spelled word that matches the definition.

6) **HIBERNATE** — HIBERNATE is the only correctly spelled word that matches the definition.

7) **MEDDLE** — MEDDLE is the only correctly spelled word that matches the definition.

8) **ECCENTRIC** — ECCENTRIC is the only correctly spelled word that matches the definition.

9) **HAPHAZARD** — HAPHAZARD is the only correctly spelled word that matches the definition.

10) **DAINTILY** — DAINTILY is the only correctly spelled word that matches the definition.

11) **FAULTLESS** — FAULTLESS is the only correctly spelled word that matches the definition.

12) **GUIDANCE** — GUIDANCE is the only correctly spelled word that matches the definition.

13) **DEARTH** — DEARTH is the only correctly spelled word that matches the definition.

14) **TUMULT** — TUMULT is the only correctly spelled word that matches the definition.

15) **PIGMENT** — PIGMENT is the only correctly spelled word that matches the definition.

16) **DISPARAGE** — DISPARAGE is the only correctly spelled word that matches the definition.

17) **FABRICATE** — FABRICATE is the only correctly spelled word that matches the definition.

18) **RIGOROUS** — RIGOROUS is the only correctly spelled word that matches the definition.

### Page 3 — Anagrams

1) **VACANT** — VACANT is the only correctly spelled word that fits the sentence.

2) **DIVERT** — DIVERT is the only correctly spelled word that fits the sentence.

3) **VARIABLE** — VARIABLE is the only correctly spelled word that fits the sentence.

4) **VALIANTLY** — VALIANTLY is the only correctly spelled word that fits the sentence.

5) **DORMANT** — DORMANT is the only correctly spelled word that fits the sentence.

6) **IMMINENT** — IMMINENT is the only correctly spelled word that fits the sentence.

7) **EXTINCT** — EXTINCT is the only correctly spelled word that fits the sentence.

8) **COAXED** — COAXED is the only correctly spelled word that fits the sentence.

9) **STRATEGY** — STRATEGY is the only correctly spelled word that fits the sentence.

10) **HYGIENE** — HYGIENE is the only correctly spelled word that fits the sentence.

11) **IMITATE** — IMITATE is the only correctly spelled word that fits the sentence.

12) **EXPLICIT** — EXPLICIT is the only correctly spelled word that fits the sentence.

13) **ALLOCATED** — ALLOCATED is the only correctly spelled word that fits the sentence.

14) **INCESSANT** — INCESSANT is the only correctly spelled word that fits the sentence.

15) **POMPOUS** — POMPOUS is the only correctly spelled word that fits the sentence.

16) **HYPOCRITE** — HYPOCRITE is the only correctly spelled word that fits the sentence.

17) **REPTILIAN** — REPTILIAN is the only correctly spelled word that fits the sentence.

18) **JUDICIOUS** — JUDICIOUS is the only correctly spelled word that fits the sentence.

### Page 4 — Spelling Mistakes

1) **B** — 'torpedos' should be 'torpedoes' — some words ending in 'o' add 'es' to make the plural.

2) **C** — 'acheivable' should be 'achievable' — the rule is: 'i' before 'e' except after 'c'.

3) **C** — 'perceptian' should be 'perception' — the ending should be 'tion'.

4) **D** — 'questionaire' should be 'questionnaire' — the suffix is 'aire', but you also need to double the 'n' in 'question'.

5) **B** — 'invigerating' should be 'invigorating' — there should be an 'o' rather than an 'e' between the 'g' and 'r'.

6) **A** — 'nusance' should be 'nuisance' — there should be an 'i' between the 'u' and the 's'.

7) **C** — 'complement' should be 'compliment'. These words are homophones — 'compliment' is correct because it means 'an expression of praise'.

8) **A** — 'rappor' should be 'rapport' — there is a silent 't' at the end of the word.

9) **D** — 'inferstructure' should be 'infrastructure' — the prefix should be 'infra'.

10) **C** — 'credable' should be 'credible' — the ending should be 'ible'.

11) **B** — 'delapidated' should be 'dilapidated' — the beginning should be 'di'.

12) **B** — 'rest' should be 'wrest'. These words are homophones — 'wrest' is correct because it means 'pull from someone's grasp with force'.

## Page 5 — Spelling Mistakes

1) **A** — 'inaugurel' should be 'inaugural' — the ending should be 'al'.

2) **C** — 'ajacent' should be 'adjacent' — there is a silent 'd' before the 'j'.

3) **B** — 'troops' should be 'troupes'. These words are homophones — 'troupes' is correct because it means 'groups of touring entertainers'.

4) **A** — 'concieve' should be 'conceive' — the rule is: 'i' before 'e' except after 'c'.

5) **B** — 'alumnuses' should be 'alumni' — this is an irregular plural.

6) **A** — 'conscientous' should be 'conscientious' — the ending should be 'tious'.

7) **C** — 'millenium' should be 'millennium' — there should be a double 'n' between the 'e' and the second 'i'.

8) **C** — 'antequity' should be 'antiquity' — the beginning should be 'anti'.

9) **A** — 'beseiged' should be 'besieged' — the rule is: 'i' before 'e' except after 'c'.

10) **B** — 'edyfice' should be 'edifice' — there should be an 'i' rather than a 'y' between the 'd' and 'f'.

11) **C** — 'gambled' should be 'gambolled'. These words are homophones — 'gambolled' is correct because it means 'ran or jumped around playfully'.

12) **A** — 'ostentacious' should be 'ostentatious' — the ending should be 'tious'.

13) **D** — 'idiosincrasies' should be 'idiosyncrasies' — there should be a 'y' rather than an 'i' in between the 's' and the 'n'.

14) **A** — 'transiant' should be 'transient' — the ending should be 'ent'.

# Section Two — Word Meanings

## Page 6 — Multiple Meanings

1) **fuse** — 'fuse' can mean 'to join together' or 'to cause an electrical appliance to stop working'.

2) **shroud** — 'shroud' can mean 'a piece of cloth covering something' or 'to conceal from view'

3) **even** — 'even' can mean 'without variation' or 'equal in value'.

4) **glossy** — 'glossy' can mean 'shiny' or 'expensive-looking'.

5) **row** — 'row' can mean 'a line of things' or 'an argument'.

6) **waste** — 'waste' can mean 'an infertile piece of land' or 'to use carelessly'.

7) **modest** — 'modest' can mean 'relatively small in amount' or 'simple'.

8) **gore** — 'gore' can mean 'blood that has been shed violently' or 'to stab with a horn'.

9) **immerse** — 'immerse' can mean 'to submerge in liquid' or 'to involve oneself deeply in an activity'.

10) **compound** — 'compound' can mean 'a combination' or 'to make something worse'.

11) **clutch** — 'clutch' can mean 'a small group' or 'to grab'.

12) **erect** — 'erect' can mean 'to construct something' or 'rigidly upright'.

13) **divine** — 'divine' can mean 'to work out' or 'delightful'.

14) **relate** — 'relate' can mean 'to connect' or 'to narrate'.

15) **flourish** — 'flourish' can mean 'to wave something to attract attention' or 'to grow in a healthy way'.

16) **embellish** — 'embellish' can mean 'to make attractive by adding decoration' or 'to add extra details to a story'.

17) **inflexible** — 'inflexible' can mean 'not able to be bent' or 'unwilling to change'.

18) **thrust** — 'thrust' can mean 'the general idea' or 'to push violently'.

## Page 7 — Multiple Meanings

1) **occupation** — 'occupation' can mean 'the act of controlling something' or 'a profession'.

2) **strained** — 'strained' can mean 'tense in atmosphere' or 'showing signs of tiredness'.

3) **outline** — 'outline' can mean 'lines showing the shape of an object' or 'a general description of the key details'.

4) **frequent** — 'frequent' can mean 'to visit a place' or 'occurring on many occasions in quick succession'.

5) **stomach** — 'stomach' can mean 'to put up with something' or 'a desire for something'.

6) **leave** — 'leave' can mean 'authorisation' or 'to go away'.

7) **bond** — 'bond' can mean 'friendship' or 'to attach securely'.

8) **entertain** — 'entertain' can mean 'to take something into consideration' or 'to provide with amusement'.

9) **realise** — 'realise' can mean 'to become fully aware of' or 'to accomplish'.

10) **removed** — 'removed' can mean 'so far away as to be different from something' or 'got rid of'.

11) **digest** — 'digest' can mean 'to break down food for absorption into the body' or 'to understand through a period of reflection'.

12) **resigned** — 'resigned' can mean 'voluntarily left a job' or 'willing to accept something unpleasant'.

13) **pile** — 'pile' can mean 'a large imposing building' or 'a heap of objects'.

14) **hack** — 'hack' can mean 'an unoriginal journalist' or 'to cut roughly'.

15) **pronounce** — 'pronounce' can mean 'to speak clearly' or 'to formally announce'.

16) **delicacy** — 'delicacy' can mean 'sensitivity when dealing with serious issues' or 'daintiness'.

17) **foundation** — 'foundation' can mean 'organisation' or 'founding principal'.

18) **grand** — 'grand' can mean 'impressive in appearance' or 'the most important version'.

19) **routed** — 'routed' can mean 'directed along a specific route' or 'beaten and made to retreat'.

20) **hone** — 'hone' can mean 'to sharpen a blade' or 'to perfect'.

21) **graft** — 'graft' can mean 'to attach something onto another object' or 'hard work'.

## Page 8 — Closest Meaning

1) **venomous** — Both words mean 'producing poison'.

2) **contemporary** — Both words mean 'happening now'.

3) **nonexistent** — Both words mean 'not present'.

4) **foretell** — Both words mean 'to say what will happen in the future'.

5) **suppress** — Both words mean 'to prevent the spreading of information'.

6) **concord** — Both words mean 'agreement'.

7) **oblivious** — Both words mean 'unaware of what is happening'.

8) **fanatical** — Both words mean 'having strong feelings about something'.

9) **gratified** — Both words mean 'satisfied'.

10) **drench** — Both words mean 'to cover with liquid'.

11) **wanderer** — Both words mean 'someone who travels from place to place'.

12) **waylay** — Both words mean 'to hold up'.

13) **celebrity** — Both words mean 'the state of being well known'.

14) **evocative** — Both words mean 'bringing memories to mind'.

15) **cleave** — Both words mean 'to split'.

16) **encroach** — Both words mean 'to go somewhere uninvited'.

17) **deprecate** — Both words mean 'to disapprove'.

18) **debonair** — Both words mean 'confident, stylish and charming'.

19) **grandiose** — Both words mean 'impressive in appearance'.

20) **ubiquitous** — Both words mean 'found everywhere'.

## Page 9 — Closest Meaning

1) **proposal** — Both words mean 'an idea put forward for consideration'.

2) **wasteful** — Both words mean 'spending money carelessly'.

3) **honoured** — Both words mean 'worthy of admiration'.

4) **wrench** — Both words mean 'a sudden pull'.

5) **compel** — Both words mean 'to forcibly persuade someone to do something'.

6) **outrageous** — Both words mean 'shocking'.

7) **automatic** — Both words mean 'done without thought'.

8) **salvage** — Both words mean 'to save something'.

9) **picturesque** — Both words are adjectives describing something visually beautiful.

10) **plagiarise** — Both words mean 'to reproduce someone else's work'.

11) **recommend** — Both words mean 'to put forward with approval'.

12) **tranquillity** — Both words mean 'a state of rest'.

13) **idolise** — Both words mean 'to admire excessively'.

14) **jaded** — Both words mean 'lacking enthusiasm'.

15) **beguile** — Both words mean 'to enchant'.

16) **subterranean** — Both words mean 'beneath the ground'.

17) **timorous** — Both words mean 'anxious or fearful'.

18) **arrogant** — Both words describe people who have an exaggerated sense of their own importance.

19) **accost** — Both words mean 'to approach and speak to someone boldly'.

20) **auspicious** — Both words mean 'likely to succeed'.

## Page 10 — Opposite Meaning

1) **manufactured** — 'homemade' means 'made at home', whereas 'manufactured' means 'made in a factory'.

2) **inhospitable** — 'welcoming' means 'friendly', whereas 'inhospitable' means 'unfriendly'.

3) **anarchy** — 'order' means 'when everything is in its correct place', whereas 'anarchy' means 'a state of disorder'.

4) **frivolous** — 'solemn' means 'serious', whereas 'frivolous' means 'not serious'.

5) **abnormal** — 'habitual' means 'usual', whereas 'abnormal' means 'different from what is usual'.

6) **euphoric** — 'despondent' means 'in low spirits', whereas 'euphoric' means 'extremely happy'.

7) **harmonious** — 'discordant' means 'tuneless', whereas 'harmonious' means 'tuneful'.

8) **deceitful** — 'sincere' means 'honest', whereas 'deceitful' means 'dishonest'.

9) **mitigate** — 'aggravate' means 'to make worse', whereas 'mitigate' means 'to make better'.

10) **inane** — 'sensible' means 'showing good sense', whereas 'inane' means 'silly and lacking sense'.

11) **pacifying** — 'provoking' means 'causing agitation', whereas 'pacifying' means 'ending agitation'.

12) **discerning** — 'uncritical' means 'lacking in judgement', whereas 'discerning' means 'having good judgement'.

13) **self-effacing** — 'conceited' means 'arrogant', whereas 'self-effacing' means 'humble'.

14) **proliferate** — 'dwindle' means 'to reduce in number', whereas 'proliferate' means 'to increase in number'.

15) **substantiate** — 'refute' means 'to disprove', whereas 'substantiate' means 'to prove'.

16) **hackneyed** — 'fresh' means 'original', whereas 'hackneyed' means 'unoriginal'.

17) **laconic** — 'long-winded' means 'using lots of words', whereas 'laconic' means 'using very few words'.

18) **assiduous** — 'negligent' means 'careless', whereas 'assiduous' means 'thorough'.

19) **disobedient** — 'docile' means 'cooperative', whereas 'disobedient' means 'uncooperative'.

20) **equanimity** — 'anxiety' means 'nervousness', whereas 'equanimity' means 'calmness'.

## Page 11 — Opposite Meaning

1) **vet**eran — 'apprentice' means 'a person who is new to a field', whereas 'veteran' means 'a person who has extensive experience in a field'.

2) **imp**artial — 'biased' means 'unfairly prejudiced for or against someone', whereas 'impartial' means 'treating everyone equally'.

3) **forsa**ke — 'keep' means 'to retain possession of', whereas 'forsake' means 'to abandon'.

4) **stric**t — 'easygoing' means 'relaxed', whereas 'strict' means 'rigidly enforced'.

5) **confoun**d — 'enlighten' means 'to improve someone's understanding', whereas 'confound' means 'to confuse someone'.

6) **nemesis** — 'friend' means 'someone you have a close relationship with', whereas 'nemesis' means 'an enemy'.

7) **slovenly** — 'smart' means 'clean and tidy', whereas 'slovenly' means 'dirty and untidy'.

8) **al**oof — 'familiar' means 'friendly', whereas 'aloof' means 'distant and unfriendly'.

9) **eva**sive — 'straightforward' means 'clear and open', whereas 'evasive' means 'indirect and difficult to pin down'.

10) **fortuitou**s — 'unlucky' means 'having bad luck', whereas 'fortuitous' means 'happening by good luck'.

11) **deri**de — 'praise' means 'to express admiration of', whereas 'deride' means 'to express contempt for'.

12) **n**aive — 'worldly' means 'experienced', whereas 'naive' means 'lacking experience'.

13) **culpab**le — 'innocent' means 'not deserving of blame', whereas 'culpable' means 'deserving blame'.

14) **en**rage — 'mollify' means 'to lessen someone's anger' whereas 'enrage' means 'to anger'.

15) **com**pliant — 'uncooperative' means 'unwilling to do what others ask', whereas 'compliant' means 'willing to do what others ask'.

16) **frail**ty — 'vigour' means 'physical strength', whereas 'frailty' means 'physical weakness'.

17) **fur**tive — 'open' means 'not concealing one's feelings', whereas 'furtive' means 'secretive'.

18) **insipi**d — 'delicious' means 'tasty', whereas 'insipid' means 'tasteless'.

19) **im**agin**ary** — 'tangible' means 'existing in reality', whereas 'imaginary' means 'only existing in the mind'.

20) **commen**d — 'vilify' means 'to describe in a disrespectful way', whereas 'commend' means 'to describe in an approving way'.

## Page 12 — Odd One Out

1) **mountain** — The other three all mean 'highest point'.

2) **dodo** — The other three are all types of birds that still exist.

3) **claim** — The other three all mean 'to declare intent'.

4) **pressurise** — The other three all mean 'to fill with an urge to do something'.

5) **excavate** — The other three all mean 'to find'.

6) **novice** — The other three all mean 'expert'.

7) **grave** — The other three all mean 'fatal'.

8) **auditor** — The other three are all people who speak publicly.

9) **wail** — The other three all mean 'to grieve'.

10) **article** — The other three are all types of punctuation.

11) **suspect** — The other three are all convicted criminals.

12) **harrowing** — The other three all mean 'frightening or threatening'.

13) **fortress** — The other three are all defensive features of a castle.

14) **organism** — The other three all mean 'a person or animal's children'.

15) **monarch** — The other three all mean 'cruel and oppressive ruler'.

16) **biography** — The other three are all genres of fiction books.

17) **standstill** — The other three are all verbs that mean 'stop'.

18) **cliché** — The other three all mean 'a short expression that contains a general truth'.

## Page 13 — Odd One Out

1) **eager** — The other three are all adverbs relating to time.

2) **vexation** — The other three all mean 'a feeling of happiness'.

3) **negotiate** — The other three all mean 'to be indecisive'.

4) **willow** — The other three are all types of flowers.

5) **allure** — The other three all mean 'excessive self-admiration'.

6) **visual** — The other three are mean 'evident'.

7) **impromptu** — The other three all mean 'straightforward and honest'.

8) **stalk** — The other three are all items of fishing equipment.

9) **ignite** — The other three all mean 'to burn'.

10) **Mongolia** — The other three are all South American countries.

11) **power** — The other three are all forms of energy.

12) **trombone** — The other three are all woodwind instruments.

13) **sumptuous** — The other three all mean 'existing in large quantities'.

14) **socialise** — The other three all mean 'to mix together'.

15) **inessential** — The other three all mean 'essential'.

16) **discreet** — The other three all mean 'shrewd'.

17) **delay** — The other three all mean 'to keep something from happening'.

18) **forefront** — The other three all mean 'outer appearance'.

19) **ligament** — The other three are all bones in the human body.

20) **Dublin** — The other three are all cities in the United Kingdom.

21) **chronology** — The other three all mean 'a period of time'.

22) **dilated** — The other three all mean 'excessive'.

## Page 14 — Reorder Words to Make a Sentence

Your child may have made a different sentence using the words given. This is fine, as long as the correct word has been chosen.

1) **shirt** — The words can be rearranged into the sentence 'I know someone who only wears pink clothes.'

2) **aboard** — The words can be rearranged into the sentence 'I want to be a sailor but I get seasick.'

3) **by** — The words can be rearranged into the sentence 'The bus was delayed so we missed the concert.'

4) **before** — The words can be rearranged into the sentence 'Charlie has not seen the dentist since he was eight.'

5) **repair** — The words can be rearranged into the sentence 'The road is blocked because there was a traffic accident.'

6) **old** — The words can be rearranged into the sentence 'Priya started competing in gymnastics three years ago.'

7) **chapters** — The words can be rearranged into the sentence 'The book I was reading ended on a thrilling cliffhanger.'

8) **most** — The words can be rearranged into the sentence 'My sister thinks that I am the dullest person ever.'

9) **munched** — The words can be rearranged into the sentence 'The naughty horse refused to eat the juicy carrot.'

10) **once** — The words can be rearranged into the sentence 'Tina chose her outfit and then got dressed.'

11) **loudly** — The words can be rearranged into the sentence 'Jodie paused the song because she did not like the lyrics.'

12) **cheer** — The words can be rearranged into the sentence 'The entire audience rose to its feet and applauded.'

13) **join** — The words can be rearranged into the sentence 'The local rowing club is advertising for new members.'

14) **begins** — The words can be rearranged into the sentence 'We went for a walk before it started to rain.'

15) **sting** — The words can be rearranged into the sentence 'Leo ran until his feet were covered in blisters.'

16) **failure** — The words can be rearranged into the sentence 'My party was a success despite the cake burning.'

17) **more** — The words can be rearranged into the sentence 'Fishing seems boring but it can be an exciting sport.'

18) **cliff** — The words can be rearranged into the sentence 'The adventurous explorer trekked through the dangerous jungle.'

## Page 15 — Reorder Words to Make a Sentence

Your child may have made a different sentence using the words given. This is fine, as long as the correct word has been chosen.

1) **leaves** — The words can be rearranged into the sentence 'I am excited because a flower has bloomed on my cactus.'

2) **on** — The words can be rearranged into the sentence 'The strict teacher told Kamil off for daydreaming during her lesson.'

3) **liked** — The words can be rearranged into the sentence 'They would have arrived earlier but their train broke down.'

4) **since** — The words can be rearranged into the sentence 'We sampled every type of cake before we chose our favourite.'

5) **during** — The words can be rearranged into the sentence 'Take care when walking back from school in the dark.'

6) **told** — The words can be rearranged into the sentence 'The burger was too filling so I let my brother finish it.'

7) **ends** — The words can be rearranged into the sentence 'My computer started making noises and then the screen went black.'

8) **at** — The words can be rearranged into the sentence 'Our dog covered us in mud after rolling in a puddle.'

9) **its** — The words can be rearranged into the sentence 'I smiled at the kind girl who complimented my green T-shirt.'

10) **pour** — The words can be rearranged into the sentence 'You must melt chocolate in order to make a dipping sauce.'

11) **should** — The words can be rearranged into the sentence 'Viv realised that she was meant to be in an English lesson.'

12) **damage** — The words can be rearranged into the sentence 'The letter failed to arrive because its address was illegible.'

13) **Katy** — The words can be rearranged into the sentence 'My cousin's sponsored cycle managed to raise two hundred pounds.'

14) **not** — The words can be rearranged into the sentence 'The hotly anticipated contest was a bit of a disappointment.'

15) **due** — The words can be rearranged into the sentence 'I attempted to explain the absence of my maths homework by gesticulating wildly.'

16) **those** — The words can be rearranged into the sentence 'Sam would not have managed to complete the puzzle without Sally's expertise.'

17) **closer** — The words can be rearranged into the sentence 'We moved away from the enclosure as it was clear the tiger was enraged.'

18) **by** — The words can be rearranged into the sentence 'I was scolded for telling jokes when I was meant to be sitting in silence.'

19) **shouted** — The words can be rearranged into the sentence 'The excited children flooded into the street when they heard the ice cream van.'

20) **in** — The words can be rearranged into the sentence 'My favourite season is summer because there is a long break from school.'

21) **how** — The words can be rearranged into the sentence 'Do you think that dogs prefer going on long walks or being stroked?'

22) **they** — The words can be rearranged into the sentence 'They cannot believe that their parents were once young and cool like them.'

## Page 16 — Word Connections

1) **finish** — 'cascade' and 'cease' are synonyms of 'flow' and 'finish'.

2) **colony** — 'school' and 'colony' are the collective names for a group of 'fish' and 'bats'.

3) **Illicit** — 'Illicit' and 'precarious' are antonyms of 'legal' and 'secure'.

4) **reclusive** — 'cheerful' and 'sociable' are antonyms of 'disconsolate' and 'reclusive'.

5) **publishing** — A 'doctor' and an 'editor' work in the fields of 'medicine' and 'publishing'.

6) **Ravine** — 'ravine' and 'precipice' are synonyms of 'gorge' and 'cliff'.

7) **mission** — A 'knight' and an 'agent' go on a 'quest' and a 'mission'.

8) **match** — A 'spectator' and an 'audience' watch a 'match' and a 'play'.

9) **deforestation** — 'traffic' and 'logging' can cause 'pollution' and 'deforestation'.

10) **nail** — A 'wrench' and 'hammer' are tools you use to work with a 'bolt' and 'nail'.

11) **Lunar** — 'lunar' and 'solar' are adjectives that describe things relating to the 'moon' and the 'sun'.

12) **pragmatic** — 'impulsive' and 'pragmatic' are synonyms of 'rash' and 'practical'.

13) **Speech** — A 'speech' and a 'report' are forms of writing that are intended to 'persuade' and 'inform'.

14) **breeze** — 'breeze' and 'drizzle' are light versions of wind and rain, whereas a 'gale' and a 'downpour' are extreme versions.

15) **benign** — 'threatening' and 'hostile' are antonyms of 'innocuous' and 'benign'.

16) **status** — 'deceit' and 'status' are synonyms of 'fraud' and 'prestige'.

17) **energetic** — 'slothful' and 'significant' are antonyms of 'energetic' and 'trifling'.

18) **Pew** — A 'pew' and a 'sofa' are types of seat found in a 'chapel' and a 'lounge'.

19) **novel** — 'Prose' and 'verse' are types of writing used in a 'novel' and a 'poem'.

20) **uphold** — 'withdraw' and 'defend' are synonyms of 'revoke' and 'uphold'.

## Page 17 — Word Connections

1) **convey** — A 'barrier' and an 'aqueduct' are used to 'prevent' things getting through and 'convey' water across a valley.

2) **ingenious** — 'creative' and 'wise' are synonyms of 'ingenious' and 'informed'.

3) **knowledgeable** — 'exercise' and 'study' can cause a person to become 'muscular' and 'knowledgeable'.

4) **Goodwill** — 'goodwill' and 'generosity' are antonyms of 'malice' and 'generosity'.

5) **excess** — 'plethora' and 'variety' are synonyms of 'excess' and 'diversity'.

6) **centaur** — A 'mermaid' is half-human half-'fish', and a 'centaur' is half-human half-'horse'.

7) **soar** — 'strut' and 'soar' describe the way that a 'cockerel' and an 'eagle' move.

8) **student** — 'nuptials' and a 'graduation' are events to celebrate the love of a 'couple' and the achievements of a 'student'.

9) **navigate** — a 'calculator' and a 'compass' are used to 'compute' and to 'navigate'.

10) **sublime** — 'exalted' and 'dire' are synonyms of 'sublime' and 'abysmal'.

11) **Enlighten** — 'enlighten' and 'dishearten' are antonyms of 'perplex' and 'uplift'.

12) **console** — You 'celebrate' someone's 'achievement' and 'console' their 'failure'.

13) **nonchalant** — 'shrug' and 'tremble' and things you do when you feel 'nonchalant' and 'afraid'.

14) **infirm** — 'unanimous' and 'frail' are synonyms of 'united' and 'infirm'.

15) **trudge** — 'skip' and 'enthuse' are enthusiastic ways to walk and talk, whereas 'trudge' and 'mutter' are unenthusiastic ways.

16) **pretentious** — 'poignant' and 'affected' are synonyms of 'affecting' and 'pretentious'.

17) **Pacifist** — A 'pacifist' and a 'vegetarian' object to going to 'war' and eating 'meat'.

18) **pigs** — 'bovine' and 'porcine' are adjectives relating to 'cows' and 'pigs'.

19) **space** — 'terrestrial' and 'celestial' are adjectives that describe things relating to the 'Earth' and 'space'.

20) **guile** — 'decency' and 'guile' are synonyms of 'decorum' and 'cunning'.

21) **nervous** — The 'heart' and the 'brain' are parts of the 'circulatory' and 'nervous' systems in the body.

22) **placid** — 'apoplectic' and 'goad' are antonyms of 'placid' and 'calm'.

## Page 18 — Definitions

1) **breadth** — 'breadth' means 'width or span'.

2) **hearth** — 'hearth' means 'floor of a fireplace'.

3) **wither** — 'wither' means 'to become shrivelled'.

4) **fiasco** — 'fiasco' means 'a complete failure'.

5) **idyllic** — 'idyllic' means 'extremely beautiful'.

6) **abrasive** — 'abrasive' means 'rough and harsh'.

7) **deluge** — 'deluge' means 'a heavy fall of rain'.

8) **feral** — 'feral' means 'wild or untamed'.

9) **confiscate** — 'confiscate' means 'to officially seize'.

10) **altercation** — 'altercation' means 'a heated disagreement'.

11) **ferocity** — 'ferocity' means 'the state of being violent'.

12) **erosion** — 'erosion' means 'gradual destruction by weather'.

13) **curate** — 'curate' means 'to organise an exhibition'.

14) **outlandish** — 'outlandish' means 'bizarre or unusual'.

15) **infatuated** — 'infatuated' means 'filled with intense passion'.

16) **diminutive** — 'diminutive' means 'extremely small'.

17) **malignant** — 'malignant' means 'wanting to do harm'.

18) **bereft** — 'bereft' means 'feeling great loss'.

19) **lustrous** — 'lustrous' means 'shining and glossy'.

20) **peripheral** — 'peripheral' means 'situated on the edge'.

## Page 19 — Definitions

1) **adherent** — 'adherent' means 'a follower or supporter'.

2) **cacophony** — 'cacophony' means 'a jarring mix of sounds'.

3) **figurine** — 'figurine' means 'a small model of a human'.

4) **oscillate** — 'oscillate' means 'to swing back and forth'.

5) **dour** — 'dour' means 'relentlessly gloomy'.

6) **annihilate** — 'annihilate' means 'to destroy utterly'.

7) **ineptitude** — 'ineptitude' means 'a lack of ability'.

8) **reprieve** — 'reprieve' means 'to spare from punishment'.

9) **repercussion** — 'repercussion' means 'an unwelcome consequence'.

10) **demure** — 'demure' means 'modest and shy'.

11) **ultimatum** — 'ultimatum' means 'a final demand'.

12) **onerous** — 'onerous' means 'extremely difficult and tiring'.

13) **guttural** — 'guttural' means 'rasping and throaty'.

14) **emanate** — 'emanate' means 'to come from'.

15) **sceptical** — 'sceptical' means 'having doubts or reservations'.

16) **vindictive** — 'vindictive' means 'wanting to seek revenge'.

17) **venerable** — 'venerable' means 'respected due to age or wisdom'.

18) **nuance** — 'nuance' means 'a subtle difference'.

19) **precocious** — 'precocious' means 'having mature qualities at a young age'.

20) **belligerent** — 'belligerent' means 'aggressive and willing to fight'.

21) **diffident** — 'diffident' means 'shy and lacking self-confidence'.

22) **adage** — 'adage' means 'a saying or proverb'.

# Section Three — Completing Passages

## Page 20 — Choose a Word

1) **had** — 'I **had** never understood'
2) **appeal** — 'the **appeal** of ballet'
3) **absence** — 'bored by the **absence** of dialogue'
4) **spellbound** — 'I was **spellbound** from the moment'
5) **sprang** — 'the silent dancers **sprang** into life'
6) **specially** — '**specially** appointed by a government'
7) **body** — 'or other official **body**'
8) **although** — '**although** the position entails'
9) **entails** — 'the position **entails** no official duties'
10) **expected** — 'the poet laureate is **expected**'
11) **long-standing** — 'My **long-standing** interest in volcanoes'
12) **traced** — 'can be **traced** back to my childhood'
13) **geology** — 'a **geology** graduate with a passion'
14) **passion** — 'with a **passion** for volcanology'
15) **active** — 'one of the most volcanically **active** places'

## Page 21 — Choose a Word

1) **home** — 'Brownsea Island is **home** to'
2) **abundance** — 'home to an **abundance** of wildlife'
3) **species** — 'including several protected **species** of bird'
4) **Additionally** — '**Additionally**, the island is notable'
5) **host** — 'playing **host** to the first Scout Camp in 1907'
6) **birthplace** — 'the **birthplace** of the modern-day Scouting and Guiding movements'
7) **etched** — 'concentration **etched** on her face'
8) **inching** — 'inching towards its conclusion'
9) **poised** — 'was finely **poised**'
10) **fewer** — 'Bella had **fewer** pieces remaining'
11) **strategic** — 'in a stronger **strategic** position'
12) **acutely** — 'she was **acutely** aware of the ticking of the clock'

## Page 22 — Fill in Missing Letters

1) ex**ped**ition — 'when an **expedition** led by'
2) suc**cee**ded — '**succeeded** in reaching'
3) com**pan**ions — 'along with four **companions**'
4) con**tin**ent — 'on the edge of the Antarctic **continent**'
5) sa**fel**y — 'returned **safely** in late January'
6) **r**i**val** — 'a **rival** team led by British naval officer Robert Scott'

7) sur**vived** — 'none of the party **survived** the return journey'
8) sc**rut**inised — '**scrutinised** the moody sky'
9) plu**mme**t — 'He watched a fat raindrop **plummet** to earth'
10) **n**e**arby** — 'the tin roof of a **nearby** cowshed'
11) bar**rage** — 'facing a **barrage** of bullet-like raindrops'
12) so**dden** — 'his already **sodden** hood'
13) di**rec**tion — 'in the **direction** of home'
14) inc**rea**singly — 'on the **increasingly** muddy ground'
15) land**mar**ks — 'famous London **landmarks**'
16) ic**on**ic — 'one of the most **iconic** sights in the city'
17) wi**th**in — 'the enormous bell **within** the clock tower'
18) fa**med** — 'which is **famed** for its accuracy'
19) inst**all**ed — 'was **installed** together with the bell'
20) wound — 'The clock must be **wound** three times a week'
21) p**roces**s — 'a **process** which takes more than an hour'

## Page 23 — Fill in Missing Letters

1) re**quest** — 'at her mother's **request**'
2) **S**eat**ed** — '**Seated** between her parents on the sofa'
3) eq**ual**ly — 'an **equally** dull grey skirt'
4) an**gul**ar — 'a long, bony nose and **angular** cheekbones'
5) ca**rved** — 'as if they were **carved** from stone'
6) fr**am**ing — '**framing** her face like a pair of curtains'
7) un**ner**ving — 'Most **unnerving** of all were her beady black eyes'
8) inter**change**ably — 'are often used **interchangeably**'
9) ves**sel** — 'a canoe is an open **vessel**'
10) en**clos**ed — 'kayaks are **enclosed** with a hole in the middle'
11) cru**cial** — 'Another **crucial** difference is the style of paddle'
12) pro**pel**led — 'a kayak is **propelled** forward'
13) simi**lari**ties — 'The two craft do have **similarities**'
14) alu**min**ium — 'materials, such as wood, plastic and **aluminium**'
15) sha**ft** — 'I was woken by a delicate **shaft** of sunlight'
16) im**mo**bile — 'I lay **immobile**'
17) **r**hy**thmic** — 'the **rhythmic** chug of the engine'
18) ext**ric**ate — 'managing at last to **extricate** myself'
19) oc**cur**red — 'it **occurred** to me'
20) quic**ke**ned — 'I **quickened** my step'
21) ex**pan**se — 'the **expanse** of azure ocean'

## Page 24 — Choose a Sentence

1) **C** — This is the only answer that fits with the context of the passage.

2) **C** — This is the only answer that fits with the context of the passage.

3) **A** — This is the only answer that fits with the context of the passage.

4) **B** — This is the only answer that fits with the context of the passage.

## Page 25 — Choose a Phrase

1) **The air in the room was stifling** — This is the only answer that fits with the context of the passage.

2) **intently at the door** — This is the only answer that fits with the context of the passage.

3) **thundering along the corridor** — This is the only answer that fits with the context of the passage.

4) **a grave expression** — This is the only answer that fits with the context of the passage.

5) **temporarily leave their homes** — This is the only answer that fits with the context of the passage.

6) **as a precaution** — This is the only answer that fits with the context of the passage.

7) **in the coming days** — This is the only answer that fits with the context of the passage.

8) **the outlook is gloomy** — This is the only answer that fits with the context of the passage.

# Section Four — Comprehension

## Page 26 — Finding Hidden Facts

1) **Honoka** — Honoka has two types of food: aloo gobi and curry.

2) **Abdul** — Abdul has visited four castles: Alnwick, Edlingham, Chillingham and Lindisfarne.

3) **Aarya** — Aarya rode on four trails: the purple trail, the yellow trail, the blue trail and the white trail.

4) **Todd** — Todd has two dinosaurs: the velociraptor and the triceratops.

## Page 27 — Finding Hidden Facts

1) **Xiu** — Xiu has five types of flowers: tulips, roses, pansies, daffodils and orchids.

2) **Muhammad** — Muhammad goes on two slides: Splash City and River Race.

3) **Oli** — Oli watched three films: 'Curse of the Koala', 'The Final Passengers' and 'The Galaxy's Core'.

4) **Rhys** — Rhys goes to two clubs: art club and science club.

## Page 28 — Understanding the Language in the Text

1) **B** — The fact that Ada feels like the walls are moving in suggests that the cell feels small and claustrophobic, so it is cramped and oppressive.

2) **A** — This builds anticipation because the reader wants to find out what has changed in the jailer's behaviour and what this might mean for Ada.

3) **C** — Ada has nothing to do all day in the cell, so she uses her memories to distract her from the "emptiness" of her routine.

4) **A** — The jailer is trying to avoid looking Ada in the eyes which implies he feels ashamed. This suggests that he feels guilty about how she is being treated but is afraid of facing up to his guilt.

5) **C** — By comparing Ada to a "woodlouse", the author suggests that she is being treated like an animal, rather than a human.

## Page 29 — Understanding the Language in the Text

1) **B** — Astra steers the ship by following an "obscure waymarker" in the cloud of dust. This suggests that she has her eyes fixed forward because she is focused on navigating.

2) **A** — Pictures in a pop-up book spring up suddenly when the page is turned, so this simile emphasises how suddenly the surface of the planet appears.

3) **C** — You get white knuckles from gripping something very tightly, usually because you are frightened.

4) **B** — Lucien tried telling Astra what to do and was about to "reach for the main controls", which suggests that he didn't have faith in her piloting ability. Therefore, Astra is being ironic.

5) **A** — The ship is flying through an "impenetrable cloud of crimson dust", so the description of the engines as "choking" and making occasional "startling judders" suggests that they are struggling to function.

## Page 30 — Multiple Statement Questions — Logic

1) **C** — The lowest score wins, and only one person had a lower score than Jayden, so Qadir and Maisie can't have been joint winners.

2) **A** — Finn cooks on Monday and Sunday, and Lexi cooks on Wednesday, so Imogen, Zayd and Bella cook on the remaining four days. Bella cooks two days in a row, so she doesn't cook on Tuesday, since Monday and Wednesday are already accounted for. Zayd cooks later in the week than Lexi, so he doesn't cook on Tuesday either. This means Imogen must cook on Tuesday.

3) **D** — Precious raised £5, which was less than anyone else. This means Cheng raised more than £5. Bobby raised twice as much as Cheng, so Bobby must have raised more than £10.

## Page 31 — Multiple Statement Questions — Logic

1) **C** — Jude moved in August, and Jack moved two months before him in June. Amelia moved at least six months before him, and Chloe moved three months after Amelia, which means she moved three months before Jude, so neither of them were the last to move. Maryam moved later in the year than Jack, but she also wasn't the last to move, so she must have moved in July. This means the latest Chloe moved was May, and the latest Amelia moved was February, three months before Chloe. Therefore, Maryam must have moved at least five months after Amelia.

2) **C** — Tomos's journey takes 20 minutes, and Phoebe's journey takes less time than this. Phoebe's journey takes twice as long as Luca's, so his journey takes less than 10 minutes. Niamh's journey takes 5 minutes longer than Luca's, so her journey must take less than 15 minutes.

3) **A** — Everyone visited at least 2 red checkpoints, so Zeynep scored at least 40 points from red checkpoints. She scored 80 points overall, so she scored a maximum of 40 points from blue checkpoints, meaning that she visited no more than 4 blue checkpoints. Freya visited 10 blue checkpoints and at least 2 red checkpoints, which means that she scored at least 140 points. Paige scored more points than Freya, so she scored at least 150 points. Only Elias visited more than 4 red checkpoints, so she scored a maximum of 80 points from red checkpoints. Therefore, she must have scored at least 70 points from blue checkpoints, meaning that she visited at least 7 blue checkpoints, which is more than Zeynep.

## Pages 32-34 — Mixed Comprehension Questions — Text 1

1) **B** — The poet says he wants "To see if any light-source could / Be ascertained", which means that he wanted to see if he can find the source of the light.

2) **C** — In the poem it says that the poet "had not noticed" the corridor before, so it cannot be well-known to him.

3) **A** — The poet says he enters the room "cautiously", which suggests he is nervous. He describes himself "Enjoying" the room, which suggests that he is pleased with it.

4) **D** — In the poem it says that a chair "spun" around and a "figure" said "'Good morning, friend'". This suggests that the figure was sitting in the chair and has turned around to face the poet and greet him.

5) **B** — The poet pauses to "express / Some thanks" to his friend after he is shown "an arch / Marked 'Happiness'". This suggests that the poet feels indebted to his friend for showing him the arch.

6) **D** — The poet says he feels "betrayed" when he sees "A maze of winding walls". This suggests that he didn't expect to see a maze after going through the arch.

7) **A** — Before the poet sees the door, he turns "(in hope of what?)", which suggests that he has lost hope of finding a door. When he sees the door, he feels "Eager", which suggests that he feels hope again.

8) **D** — "liberty" means 'freedom', so this suggests the poet thinks that doors can offer people freedom and choice.

9) **B** — In this context, "checked" means 'stopped'. It means that the poet pauses when he sees the corridor.

10) **C** — 'discerned' means 'made out'.

## Pages 35-37 — Mixed Comprehension Questions — Text 2

1) **D** — In the passage it says that the narrator has not had "a minute of sleep in three days", so he can't have just woken up.

2) **B** — The weather is described as "warm and overcast", while the narrator can feel the lifeboat "rocking gently", which suggests that the waves are fairly small.

3) **A** — A "stowaway" is someone who sneaks onto a ship secretly. The narrator "failed to notice" that the tiger had boarded the lifeboat, so this makes the tiger seem like a stowaway.

4) **B** — According to the passage, the tiger takes up "over a third of the length of the ship" and the lifeboat is "twenty-six feet long". One third of 26 is more than eight feet, so the tiger must be over eight feet long.

5) **D** — The narrator says that the challenger "becomes relaxed" because they have "nothing left to lose", so they play better because they no longer feel any pressure to win.

6) **A** — The passage says that it is "the morning", the tiger is a "Bengal tiger", and that "the day was like the previous one, warm and overcast, the clouds low, the breeze light". It does not mention what caused the narrator to notice the tiger.

7) **C** — The narrator says it is "Incredible" that the existence of the tiger "should need consent to be true", as "only after much deliberation" does he conclude that it is real. This suggests that he is amazed that he could be unsure whether a tiger was on board.

8) **C** — The narrator says that he "lost all hope", which would normally make someone feel bad. It's ironic that, in this case, losing hope meant that he "perked up", as it's the opposite of what you would expect.

9) **B** — "deliberation" means 'contemplation'. They both mean 'careful consideration'.

10) **A** — "insouciant" means 'carefree'. They both mean 'having no concerns'.

## Pages 38-40 — Mixed Comprehension Questions — Text 3

1) **C** — In the passage, it says that 'Yeti' is a "diesel locomotive". The first diesel locomotives were purchased "between 1986 and 1992", so 'Yeti' can't have been one of the original trains.

2) **D** — Llanberis is situated "on Snowdon's north-west flank", so passengers travelling from Llanberis to the summit would be travelling from north-west to south-east.

3) **C** — In the passage, it says that you can see "the rest of Snowdonia National Park" from the summit of Snowdon. This implies that Snowdon itself is within the national park.

4) **A** — According to the passage, Snowdon has a "harsh climate" with strong winds and low temperatures. However, the author suggests that the view from the top is "breathtaking" if seen on "a clear, still summer's day", which suggests that the weather can sometimes be more settled.

5) **A** — In the passage, it says that "enclosed roofs" were only added "from 1947" and that the first "diesel locomotives" were introduced "between 1986 and 1992". Therefore, in 1946, passengers would have ridden in open-top carriages pushed by the original steam locomotives.

6) **C** — In the passage, it says that the building that opened in 2009 replaced a building that was "demolished three years earlier", which was 2006. That building was "constructed in the 1930s". This means that the latest it could have been built was 1939. It therefore must have stood for more than 65 years.

7) **B** — In the passage, it says that the "five original steam trains" were "designed in Switzerland". Then in the early 1920s "three more Swiss steam trains" were purchased, which means that all the locomotives in operation by the 1930s were designed in Switzerland.

8) **D** — According to the passage, Sir Richard Moon came up with the idea of a Snowdon railway in 1869, but work did not begin until 25 years later, which was 1894. Work began "in December of that year" and took "16 months", which means that the railway became operational in April 1896.

9) **A** — "whimsical" means 'unusual and fanciful'. This suggests that the name 'Yeti' was a more unusual name for a train than a name like 'Snowdon'.

10) **C** — 'inclement weather' is weather that is unpleasantly cold, wet or windy.

## Pages 41-43 — Mixed Comprehension Questions — Text 4

1) **C** — The passage mentions that Catherine's "person" and "mind", as well as "the character of her father and mother", made people unlikely to think she would be a heroine, but doesn't mention the size of her family as one of the reasons.

2) **C** — The passage says Catherine was "very fond of tinkling the keys of the old forlorn spinnet", which shows that she had tried to play an instrument before having music lessons.

3) **A** — Catherine was "fond of all boy's plays" and "greatly preferred cricket" to playing with "dolls". This shows that she was not interested in the kinds of things that girls her age were expected to be interested in at the time, meaning that she was an unconventional child.

4) **B** — The passage does not say that he is a controlling father. It says that Catherine's father "was not in the least addicted to locking up his daughters". This suggests that he is not controlling when it comes to his daughters' actions.

5) **D** — The passage says that "what is more remarkable" is her "good constitution", because "instead of dying" giving birth to Catherine, she went on to "have six children more" and "enjoy excellent health herself".

6) **B** — The passage says that Catherine couldn't "learn or understand anything before she was taught", which shows she struggled to learn anything by herself.

7) **C** — The phrase means Mrs. Morland didn't want to force her daughters to succeed at something they didn't like or weren't skilled at.

8) **D** — The passage says Mrs. Morland "had three sons before Catherine was born", and after Catherine was born she had "six children more". This means Catherine was the first-born daughter, so her sister Sally can't be older than her.

9) **C** — "lank" means 'lifeless'.

10) **B** — "conjectured" means 'supposed'.

# Assessment Tests

## Pages 44-49 — Assessment Test 1

1) **C** — In the passage, Liana observes "the sun's slow descent". This suggests that the sun is setting, so it must be evening.

2) **B** — In the passage, it says that Liana rings the bell to "alert the other lookouts", which suggests that Liana is also a lookout.

3) **D** — In the passage, it says that the lookouts are planning to "flee with the news to where the queen's army was stationed".

4) **D** — When Liana sees the army, she rings the alarm bell "Without hesitation". This suggests that she acts quickly and decisively — 'decisively' means 'making decisions quickly and effectively'.

5) **B** — As Liana walks through her village, she has a "feeling of nostalgia". 'Nostalgia' is a sentimental attachment to a place due to happy memories of the past, so this description suggests Liana has a strong personal attachment to the village.

6) **B** — In the passage, Liana notices that the "shadows were expanding too quickly compared to the sun's slow descent".

7) **C** — In the passage, it says that "The dreaded moment was upon them" after Liana spots the army. This suggests that the lookouts were expecting the army's arrival.

8) **A** — The village is described as a "hilltop village" and the army has to "climb from the valley to the village walls". This suggests that the village is above a valley rather than in one.

9) **B** — The passage does not mention what the temperature is like outside.

10) **B** — "hue" means 'colour'. They can both mean 'shade'.

11) **A** — "mundane" means 'unremarkable'. They both mean 'not particularly interesting'.

12) **D** — "panoramic" means 'wide'. They can both mean 'sweeping'.

13) **C** — "the elements" means 'the weather'. If you abandon something to the elements, it means you leave it without protection from the weather.

14) **C** — "dwelling on" means 'thinking about', so the phrase means 'thinking about that now wouldn't do any good'.

15) **pronounce** — The other three all mean 'to highlight'.

16) **soothe** — The other three all mean 'to fix'.

17) **convention** — The other three are all instructions to be followed.

18) **tether** — The other three all mean 'to permanently join into one object'.

19) **efficient** — The other three all mean 'masterly'.

20) **structure** — The other three all mean 'base'.

21) **troubadour** — The other three are names of groups.

22) **curve** — The other three are all spiral shapes.

23) **cove** — The other three are landforms that extend into a body of water.

24) **B** — 'are yet to be confirmed' is the only answer that fits with the context of the passage.

25) **C** — 'After the rumour spread nationwide' is the only answer that fits with the context of the passage.

26) **B** — 'conflicting accounts' is the only answer that fits with the context of the passage.

27) **D** — 'in recent years' is the only answer that fits with the context of the passage.

28) **subordinate** — 'subordinate' means 'a person of lower rank'.

29) **commission** — 'commission' means 'to request something be made'.

30) **indulge** — 'indulge' means 'to let oneself enjoy something'.

31) **abysmal** — 'abysmal' means 'extremely terrible'.

32) **solidarity** — 'solidarity' means 'agreement within a group'.

33) **conscious** — 'conscious' means 'aware of one's surroundings'.

34) **communicative** — 'communicative' means 'willing to talk to people'.

35) **buoyant** — 'buoyant' means 'confident and happy'.

36) **exacerbate** — 'exacerbate' means 'to make a situation worse'.

37) **aberration** — 'aberration' means 'a deviation from normality'.

38) **C** — 'priviledge' should be 'privilege' — there shouldn't be a 'd' before the 'g'.

39) **A** — 'noticable' should be 'noticeable' — there should be an 'e' between the 'c' and the 'a'.

40) **D** — 'presense' should be 'presence' — the 'c' makes an 's' sound.

41) **D** — 'ignorence' should be 'ignorance' — the suffix is 'ance'.

42) **C** — 'skilfull' should be 'skilful' — the suffix is 'ful'.

43) **A** — 'rangled' should be 'wrangled' — the 'w' is silent.

44) **outline** — 'slogan' and 'perimeter' are synonyms of 'catchphrase' and 'outline'.

45) **cygnet** — 'cygnet' and 'joey' are the names for a baby 'swan' and a baby 'kangaroo'.

46) **regulation** — 'rule' and 'guideline' are synonyms of 'regulation' and 'recommendation'.

47) **register** — 'instructions' and 'names' are what are written down in a 'manual' and a 'register'.

48) **stable** — 'rickety' and 'amateur' are antonyms of 'stable' and 'specialist'.

49) **Yield** — 'yield' and 'respire' are synonyms of 'surrender' and 'breathe'.

50) **apparent** — 'cumbersome' and 'obscure' are antonyms of 'convenient' and 'apparent'.

51) **bow** — 'bow' and 'nose' are the front parts of a 'ship' and a 'plane'.

52) **diet** — the 'brain' and 'diet' are the subjects that neuroscientists and nutritionists specialise in.

53) **unblemished** — 'everlasting' and 'flawless' are synonyms of 'eternal' and 'unblemished'.

54) **adulation** — 'condemnation' and 'learned' are antonyms of 'adulation' and 'instinctive'.

55) **convict** — 'absolve' and 'advantage' are antonyms of 'convict' and 'hindrance'.

56) **Obsidian** — 'obsidian' and 'mauve' are shades of 'black' and 'purple'.

57) **tease** — Both words mean 'to make fun of'.

58) **transaction** — Both words mean 'an exchange'.

59) **melancholy** — Both words mean 'sorrowful'.

60) **rife** — Both words mean 'commonly occurring'.

61) **affluent** — Both words mean 'rich'.

62) **forage** — Both words mean 'to search'.

63) **speculate** — Both words mean 'to form a theory without firm evidence'.

64) **outdated** — Both words mean 'out of fashion'.

65) **uncertain** — Both words mean 'unsure'.

66) **regretful** — Both words mean 'remorseful'.

67) **cryptic** — Both words mean 'obscure'.

68) **abhorred** — Both words mean 'hated'.

Answers

## Pages 50-55 — Assessment Test 2

1) **B** — The narrator describes his lodgings as "airless" and compares returning there to "suffocation", which suggests that he finds them stuffy.

2) **D** — The narrator enjoys "the divine stillness" of the heath, which suggests that he finds it peaceful and appealing. In contrast, he is not looking forward to returning to "the heat and gloom of London", which suggests that he finds London dark and oppressive.

3) **C** — The narrator decides to "follow the white winding paths across the lonely heath" and then "approach London" by "striking into the Finchley Road".

4) **A** — The narrator "thought but little on any subject", which suggests that he isn't focusing on anything in particular. However, his "mind remained open to the impressions produced by the view", which suggests he is admiring the scenery.

5) **C** — In the passage, it says that her face is "bent in grave inquiry" towards the narrator, which suggests that she is looking at the narrator rather than towards London.

6) **D** — The narrator says that he "mechanically turned" towards the road back to London, which suggests that he was acting on instinct.

7) **B** — The narrator says that "every drop of blood" in his body "was brought to a stop", which suggests that he is filled with dread, but as he turns around he tightens his fingers round the stick, which suggests that he is prepared to defend himself.

8) **B** — In the passage, it says that "the heath looked wild enough" to be "hundreds of miles away from" London. This suggests that it appears so different to London that it is hard to believe it is actually close to the city.

9) **C** — "repelled" is closest in meaning to 'repulsed'. It means 'disgusted'.

10) **D** — "alternations" is closest in meaning to 'interchanges'. It means 'repeated shifts between two things'.

11) **turbulent** — 'peaceful' means 'free from disturbance', whereas 'turbulent' means 'full of disturbance'.

12) **virtue** — 'shortcoming' means 'a fault or weakness', whereas 'virtue' means 'a strength or quality'.

13) **rupture** — 'unite' means 'join together', whereas 'rupture' means 'break apart'.

14) **inception** — 'conclusion' means 'end', whereas 'inception' means 'beginning'.

15) **disregard** — 'heed' means 'listen to', whereas 'disregard' means 'ignore'.

16) **neglect** — 'nurture' means 'care for', whereas 'neglect' means 'fail to care for'.

17) **cautious** — 'impulsive' means 'rash', whereas 'cautious' means 'careful'.

18) **persuade** — 'discourage' means 'deter', whereas 'persuade' means 'encourage'.

19) **striking** — 'nondescript' means 'lacking distinctive qualities', whereas 'striking' means 'distinctive'.

20) **courteous** — 'insolent' means 'rude', whereas 'courteous' means 'polite'.

21) **suppress** — 'unleash' means 'release', whereas 'suppress' means 'restrain'.

22) **eloquent** — 'inarticulate' means 'unable to express yourself', whereas 'eloquent' means 'able to express yourself well'.

23) **prejudiced** — 'neutral' means 'unbiased', whereas 'prejudiced' means 'biased'.

24) **ornate** — 'spartan' means 'simple and plain', whereas 'ornate' means 'intricate and decorated'.

25) **deferential** — 'disrespectful' means 'not respectful', whereas 'deferential' means 'respectful'.

26) **D** — The passage says that some villagers were "enjoying the seething rain, an antidote for the heat", so not all of them find the weather conditions uncomfortable.

27) **C** — In the passage, Komazawa watches the children play "with the same ardent wistfulness with which he habitually regarded them from the door". This suggests that the children usually play without him.

28) **B** — The passage does not mention how long Komazawa had been up the tree.

29) **D** — In the passage, Madame Aoi says that "the tree bends", which suggests it is weak. She says that it may "become angry with us and vent its vengeance upon my son", which suggests she is worried it might break and hurt Komazawa as a result.

30) **B** — 'When **most** people hear the words 'black hole''

31) **D** — 'they **visualise** a gigantic pit of darkness'

32) **B** — 'swirling **through** space and sucking in everything'

33) **B** — 'The **reality**, however, is more complicated'

34) **A** — 'more **complicated** and mysterious'

35) **D** — 'an **exceedingly** strong gravitational pull'

36) **C** — 'towards the centre **of** a black hole'

37) **D** — '**even** light cannot escape'

38) **A** — 'For this reason, black holes are **invisible**'

39) **C** — 'scientists are only able to **detect** their existence'

40) **A** — 'by observing their effect on **nearby** stars'

41) **D** — 'it **would** seem that Earth is unlikely'

42) **C** — 'Earth is **unlikely** to be sucked into a black hole'

43) **C** — '**Contrary** to popular belief'

44) **A** — '**instead**, they only affect objects'

45) **C** — 'within a **certain** area'

46) **B** — '**referred** to as their "radius of influence"'

47) **D** — 'The nearest **confirmed** black hole to Earth'

48) **A** — '**almost** 5000 light-years away'

49) **A** — 'much too far to **cause** us any concern'

50) **long** — The words can be rearranged into the sentence 'They queued for nearly an hour to enter the museum.'

51) **going** — The words can be rearranged into the sentence 'I am planning a trip to Cornwall with my grandmother.'

52) **weather** — The words can be rearranged into the sentence 'This has been one of the hottest summers on record.'

53) **while** — The words can be rearranged into the sentence 'The woman immediately called her son with some news.'

54) **in** — The words can be rearranged into the sentence 'The room was filled with a powerful aroma of curry being cooked.'

55) **foyer** — Both words mean 'a room at the front of a building'.

56) **immaculate** — Both words mean 'perfect'.

57) **rebuff** — Both words mean 'refuse'.

58) **devise** — Both words mean 'invent'.

59) **audacious** — Both words mean 'willing to take risks'.

60) **unintentional** — Both words mean 'unplanned'.

61) **tenacious** — Both words mean 'not willing to give up easily'.

62) **skulk** — Both words mean 'move in a stealthy manner'.

63) **mutiny** — Both words mean 'uprising'.

64) **desecrate** — Both words mean 'treat something special or sacred with disrespect'.

65) **salvation** — Both words mean 'the act of being rescued'.

66) **ostracise** — Both words mean 'keep out'.

67) **insubordinate** — Both words mean 'unwilling to follow rules'.

68) **obsequious** — Both words mean 'excessively obedient and flattering'.

## Pages 56-61 — Assessment Test 3

1) **C** — The poet describes the crows as "villains" who are "mischievous" and "rascally". This suggests she thinks they are wicked and sly.

2) **D** — The poet asks whether the crows went "far in carrion quest". "carrion" is rotting flesh, so this means that the crows were going in search of dead animals.

3) **D** — "inky" means 'black', and "hue" means 'colour', so the poet is referring to the crows' black feathers.

4) **B** — The beck is described as "lazy", which suggests that the current flows slowly.

5) **D** — The cottage is described as "Vale-environed". 'vale' is another word for 'valley', and 'environed' means 'surrounded', so the cottage is in a valley. The cottage is also surrounded by "emerald bands", which indicates there are green fields around it.

6) **B** — The sun rises at different times in different places around the globe, so the poet is suggesting that the crows might have travelled to distant places where the sun rises earlier.

7) **C** — The poet offers to "Absolve" the crows if they have visited "the place where" she "was born". This suggests that she will forgive them if they have visited somewhere from her past and will tell her about it.

8) **D** — The stones are "Crossing the current", which means they are in the middle of the stream, but they are "obstinate", which means that they remain fixed in place.

9) **B** — "Plunderous" means 'pilfering'. It means that the crows fly around trying to steal food.

10) **A** — "vagrant" means 'nomadic'. It means that the crows are constantly moving around and don't stay in one place for long.

11) **undoubted**ly — 'Silverstone is **undoubtedly**'

12) **orig**ins — 'Its **origins** can be traced back'

13) **turmoil** — 'the **turmoil** of World War II'

14) **popular**ity — 'steadily growing in **popularity**'

15) **enthusi**asts — 'a group of racing **enthusiasts**'

16) **potent**ial — 'discussing **potential** venues'

17) **disused** — 'a **disused** airfield near his home'

18) **staged** — 'where they **staged** a race'

19) **deemed** — 'it was **deemed** a success'

20) **transform**ed — '**transformed** the airfield'

21) **legitimate** — 'a **legitimate** race track'

22) **promin**ent — 'several **prominent** races'

23) **maiden** — 'the **maiden** Formula One World Championship race'

24) **fixture** — 'Silverstone remains a popular **fixture**'

25) **reputa**tion — 'it has a **reputation**'

26) **C** — In the text, it says that tourists come to Churchill specifically because it "sits on a polar bear migration path".

27) **D** — According to the text, "boats ferry tourists around the Hudson Bay" in the summer, so it can't remain frozen all year round.

28) **B** — In the passage, it says that 10 000 tourists visit Churchill during "Bear Season", which is "roughly ten times the number of locals". Therefore, the local population is around 1000 people. Later on, it says that the town's peak population was "nearly 2000" people. This means that the population has fallen by roughly 50%.

29) **A** — In the passage, it says that when the railway wasn't operating, Churchill's residents were only able to access "the outside world" if they could "afford air fares". This implies that Churchill is accessible by train or by plane but not by road.

30) **pastoral** — 'urban' means 'related to the city', whereas 'pastoral' means 'related to the countryside'.

31) **debunk** — 'validate' means 'confirm the truth of', whereas 'debunk' means 'expose as fake'.

32) **cajole** — 'dissuade' means 'convince someone not to do something', whereas 'cajole' means 'urge someone to do something'.

33) **flounder** — 'prosper' means 'thrive', whereas 'flounder' means 'struggle'.

34) **irrational** — 'logical' means 'reasonable and correct', whereas 'irrational' means 'unreasonable and wrong'.

35) **extol** — 'belittle' means 'put someone down', whereas 'extol' means 'praise someone's virtues'.

36) **surreptitious** — 'overt' means 'obvious and open', whereas 'surreptitious' means 'sneaky and secretive'.

37) **cogent** — 'unconvincing' means 'not persuasive', whereas 'cogent' means 'persuasive'.

38) **immutable** — 'inconstant' means 'changeable', whereas 'immutable' means 'unchanging'.

39) **gauche** — 'sophisticated' means 'refined', whereas 'gauche' means 'awkward'.

40) **contend** — 'contend' can mean 'to argue a point' or 'to fight for a victory'.

41) **rattle** — 'rattle' can mean 'to make a repeated knocking noise' or 'to cause someone to feel disconcerted'.

42) **cradle** — 'cradle' can mean 'to hold protectively' or 'a place where something began'.

43) **patent** — 'patent' can mean 'a document giving someone a right' or 'obvious'.

44) **defer** — 'defer' can mean 'to give in to another person's wishes' or 'to put off until later'.

45) **abandon** — 'abandon' can mean 'to leave' or 'a sense of being totally carefree'.

46) **warrant** — 'warrant' can mean 'a document giving authority for something' or 'to call for'.

47) **correspond** — 'correspond' can mean 'to match up' or 'to communicate by writing'.

48) **consummate** — 'consummate' can mean 'to bring to a close' or 'highly adept'.

49) **bluff** — 'bluff' can mean 'a high, steep slope' or 'to fake'.

50) **palace** — The other three are all types of religious building.

51) **chainsaw** — The other three are all non-motorised garden cutting tools.

52) **witless** — The other three all mean 'awful'.

53) **medallion** — The other three are all old British coins.

54) **stethoscope** — The other three are all things you look into.

55) **epidemic** — The other three are all types of illness.

56) **propagate** — The other three all mean 'to expand rapidly'.

57) **portend** — The other three all mean 'something that comes before something else'.

58) **glower** — The other three are all expressions made with the mouth.

59) **UNDULATING** — UNDULATING is the only correctly spelled word that fits the sentence.

60) **NOXIOUS** — NOXIOUS is the only correctly spelled word that fits the sentence.

61) **PERSISTENCE** — PERSISTENCE is the only correctly spelled word that fits the sentence.

62) **RIOTOUS** — RIOTOUS is the only correctly spelled word that fits the sentence.

63) **DISHEVELLED** — DISHEVELLED is the only correctly spelled word that fits the sentence.

64) **DISTRAUGHT** — DISTRAUGHT is the only correctly spelled word that fits the sentence.

65) **VERACITY** — VERACITY is the only correctly spelled word that fits the sentence.

66) **TREPIDATION** — TREPIDATION is the only correctly spelled word that fits the sentence.

67) **RELISHES** — RELISHES is the only correctly spelled word that fits the sentence.

68) **CATACLYSMIC** — CATACLYSMIC is the only correctly spelled word that fits the sentence.

# Progress Chart

Answer Sheets

Use this chart to keep track of your scores for the Assessment Tests.

You can do each test more than once — download extra answer sheets from cgpbooks.co.uk/11plus/answer-sheets or scan the QR code on the right.

|  | **First Go** | **Second Go** | **Third Go** |
|---|---|---|---|
| **Test 1** | Date: <br> Score: | Date: <br> Score: | Date: <br> Score: |
| **Test 2** | Date: <br> Score: | Date: <br> Score: | Date: <br> Score: |
| **Test 3** | Date: <br> Score: | Date: <br> Score: | Date: <br> Score: |

Look back at your scores once you've done all the Assessment Tests.

Each test is out of 68 marks.

Work out which kind of mark you scored most often:

**0-33 marks** — Keep working on it — these questions are designed to stretch you.

**34-53 marks** — You're doing great — these questions are really tricky.

**54-68 marks** — Wow!  You're a Verbal Reasoning star.

V6HQDE1